THE VISUAL
DICTIONARY *of*
ANIMALS

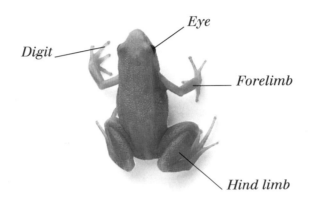

**EXTERNAL FEATURES
OF A FROG**

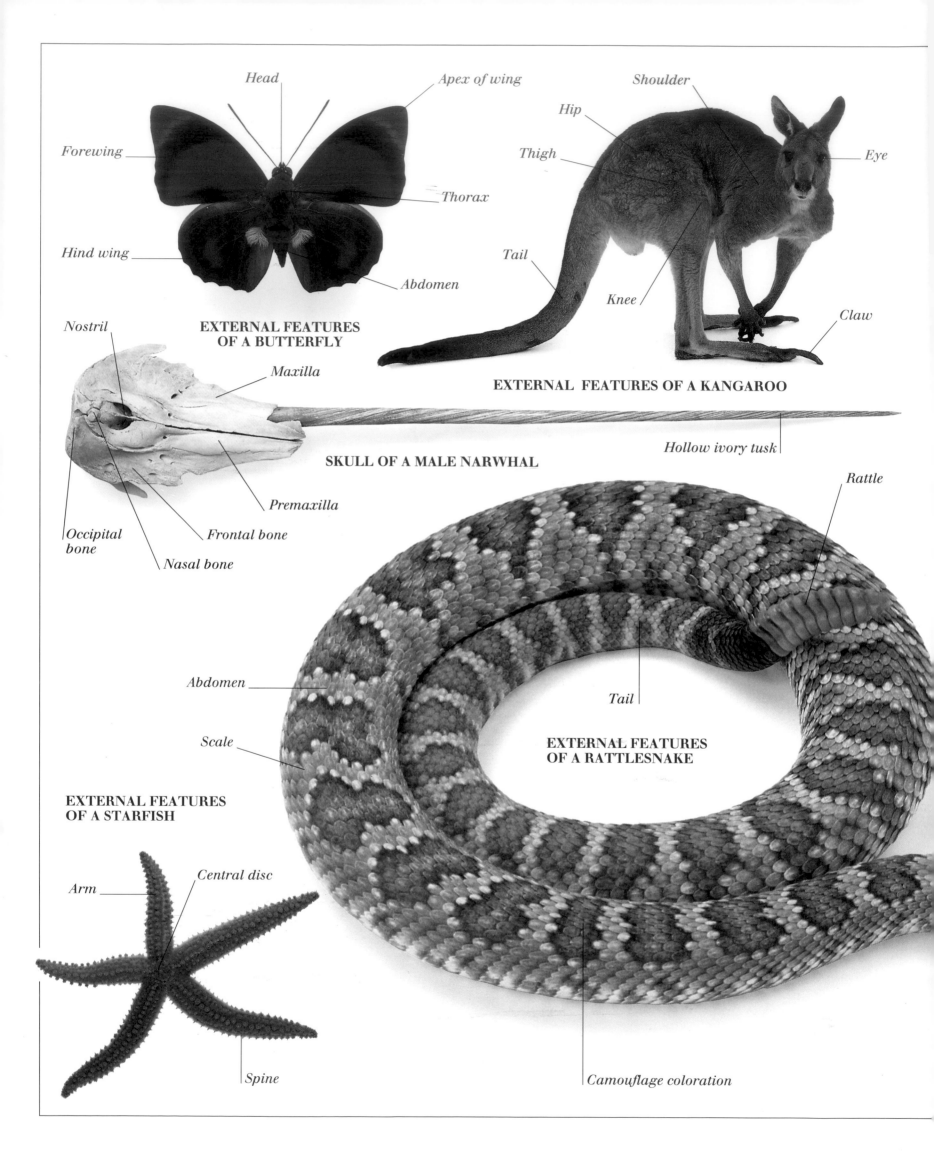

**EXTERNAL FEATURES
OF A BUTTERFLY**

Head

Apex of wing

Forewing

Thorax

Hind wing

Abdomen

EXTERNAL FEATURES OF A KANGAROO

Shoulder

Hip

Thigh

Eye

Tail

Knee

Claw

SKULL OF A MALE NARWHAL

Nostril

Maxilla

Occipital
bone

Premaxilla

Frontal bone

Nasal bone

Hollow ivory tusk

**EXTERNAL FEATURES
OF A RATTLESNAKE**

Rattle

Tail

Abdomen

Scale

Camouflage coloration

**EXTERNAL FEATURES
OF A STARFISH**

Arm

Central disc

Spine

THE VISUAL
DICTIONARY *of*
ANIMALS

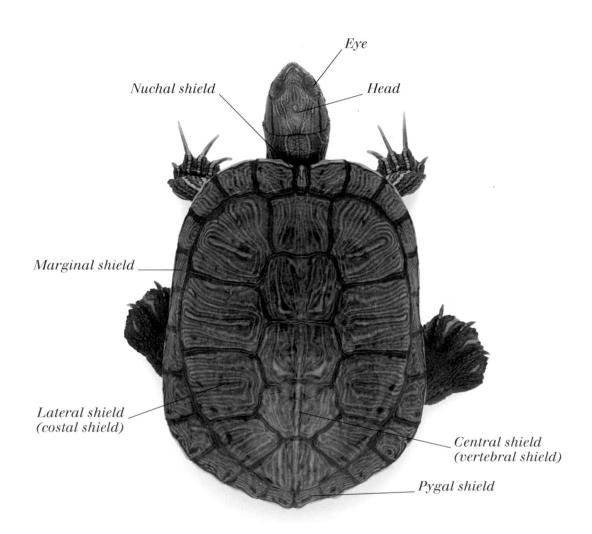

Eye

Nuchal shield

Head

Marginal shield

Lateral shield
(costal shield)

Central shield
(vertebral shield)

Pygal shield

**EXTERNAL FEATURES
OF A TERRAPIN**

COVENT
GARDEN
BOOKS

A DORLING KINDERSLEY BOOK

PROJECT ART EDITOR CLARE SHEDDEN
DESIGNER ANDREW NASH

PROJECT EDITOR MARTYN PAGE
CONSULTANT EDITOR DR RICHARD WALKER

SERIES ART EDITOR PAUL WILKINSON
ART DIRECTOR CHEZ PICTHALL
MANAGING EDITOR RUTH MIDGLEY

PHOTOGRAPHY DAVE KING, GEOFF DANN
ILLUSTRATIONS JOHN WOODCOCK, SIMONE END

PRODUCTION HILARY STEPHENS

This edition published in 1999 by Covent Garden Books

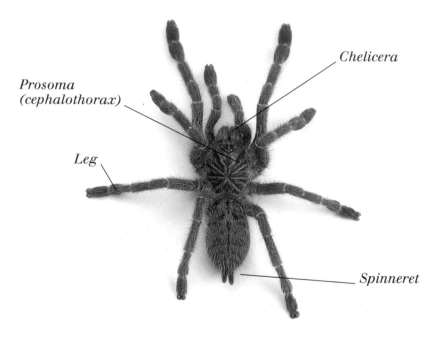

Chelicera

*Prosoma
(cephalothorax)*

Leg

Spinneret

EXTERNAL FEATURES OF A SPIDER

FIRST PUBLISHED IN GREAT BRITAIN IN 1991
BY DORLING KINDERSLEY LIMITED,
9 HENRIETTA STREET, LONDON WC2E 8PS
REPRINTED 1996.
COPYRIGHT © 1991 DORLING KINDERSLEY LIMITED, LONDON
WWW.DK.COM

A CIP CATALOGUE RECORD FOR THIS BOOK IS AVAILABLE FROM THE BRITISH LIBRARY

ISBN 1-871-854-75X

REPRODUCED BY GRB GRAFICA, VERONA, ITALY
PRINTED AND BOUND BY ARTES GRÁFICAS TOLEDO, S.A.
D.L. TO: 606 - 1999

Digit

Hind limb

Forelimb

**EXTERNAL FEATURES
OF A FROG**

Contents

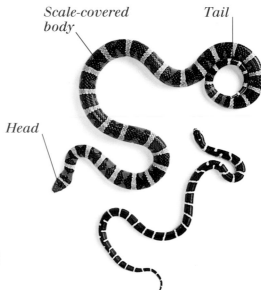

Scale-covered body

Tail

Head

**EXTERNAL FEATURES
OF A SNAKE**

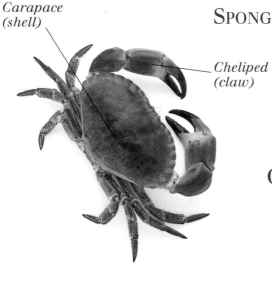

Carapace (shell)

Cheliped (claw)

**EXTERNAL FEATURES
OF A CRAB**

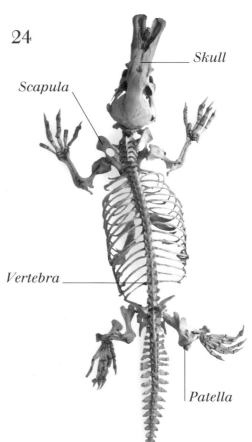

Skull

Scapula

Vertebra

Patella

SKELETON OF A PLATYPUS

Back

Eye

Forelimb

EXTERNAL FEATURES OF A RABBIT

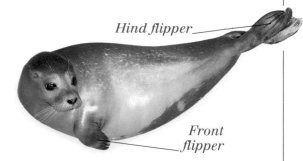

Hind flipper

Front flipper

EXTERNAL FEATURES OF A SEAL

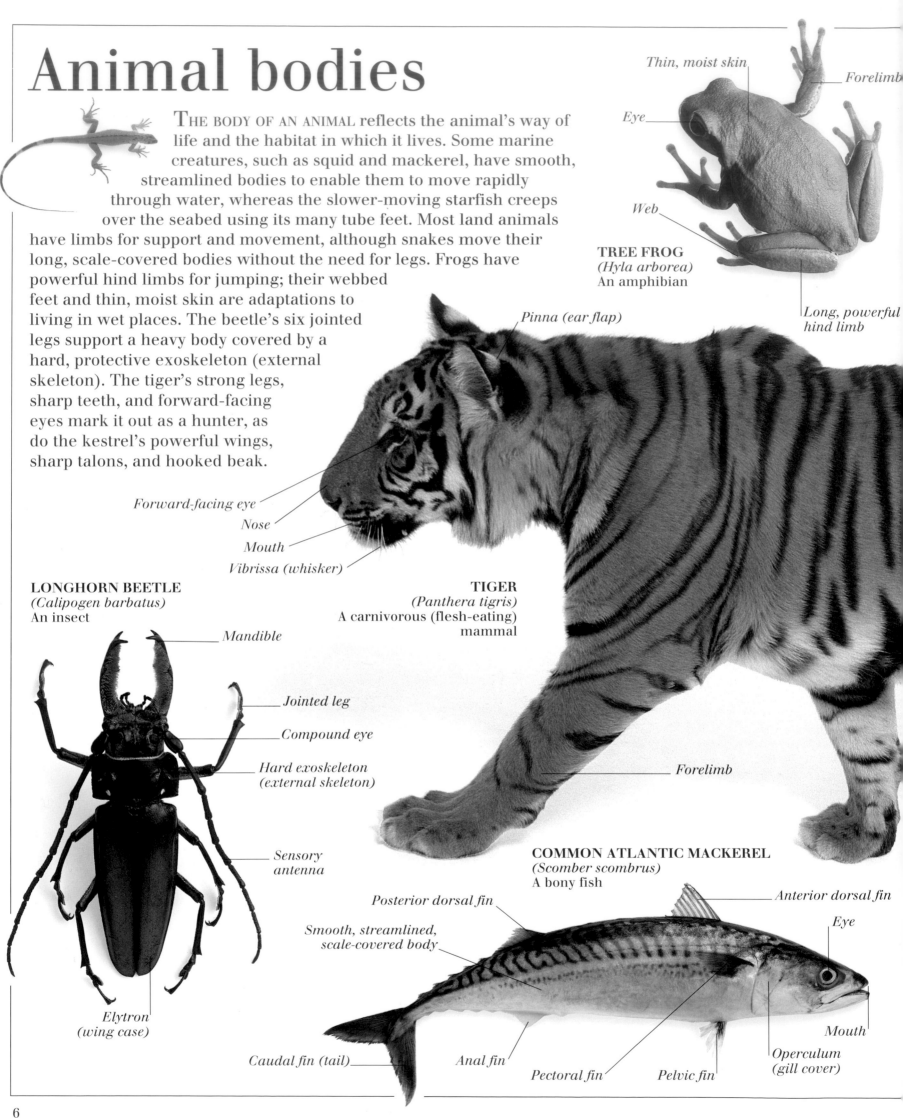

Animal bodies

THE BODY OF AN ANIMAL reflects the animal's way of life and the habitat in which it lives. Some marine creatures, such as squid and mackerel, have smooth, streamlined bodies to enable them to move rapidly through water, whereas the slower-moving starfish creeps over the seabed using its many tube feet. Most land animals have limbs for support and movement, although snakes move their long, scale-covered bodies without the need for legs. Frogs have powerful hind limbs for jumping; their webbed feet and thin, moist skin are adaptations to living in wet places. The beetle's six jointed legs support a heavy body covered by a hard, protective exoskeleton (external skeleton). The tiger's strong legs, sharp teeth, and forward-facing eyes mark it out as a hunter, as do the kestrel's powerful wings, sharp talons, and hooked beak.

Thin, moist skin

Forelimb

Eye

Web

TREE FROG
(Hyla arborea)
An amphibian

Long, powerful
hind limb

Pinna (ear flap)

Forward-facing eye

Nose

Mouth

Vibrissa (whisker)

TIGER
(Panthera tigris)
A carnivorous (flesh-eating)
mammal

LONGHORN BEETLE
(Calipogen barbatus)
An insect

Mandible

Jointed leg

Compound eye

Hard exoskeleton
(external skeleton)

Sensory
antenna

Forelimb

Elytron
(wing case)

COMMON ATLANTIC MACKEREL
(Scomber scombrus)
A bony fish

Posterior dorsal fin

Anterior dorsal fin

Smooth, streamlined,
scale-covered body

Eye

Mouth

Caudal fin (tail)

Anal fin

Pectoral fin

Pelvic fin

Operculum
(gill cover)

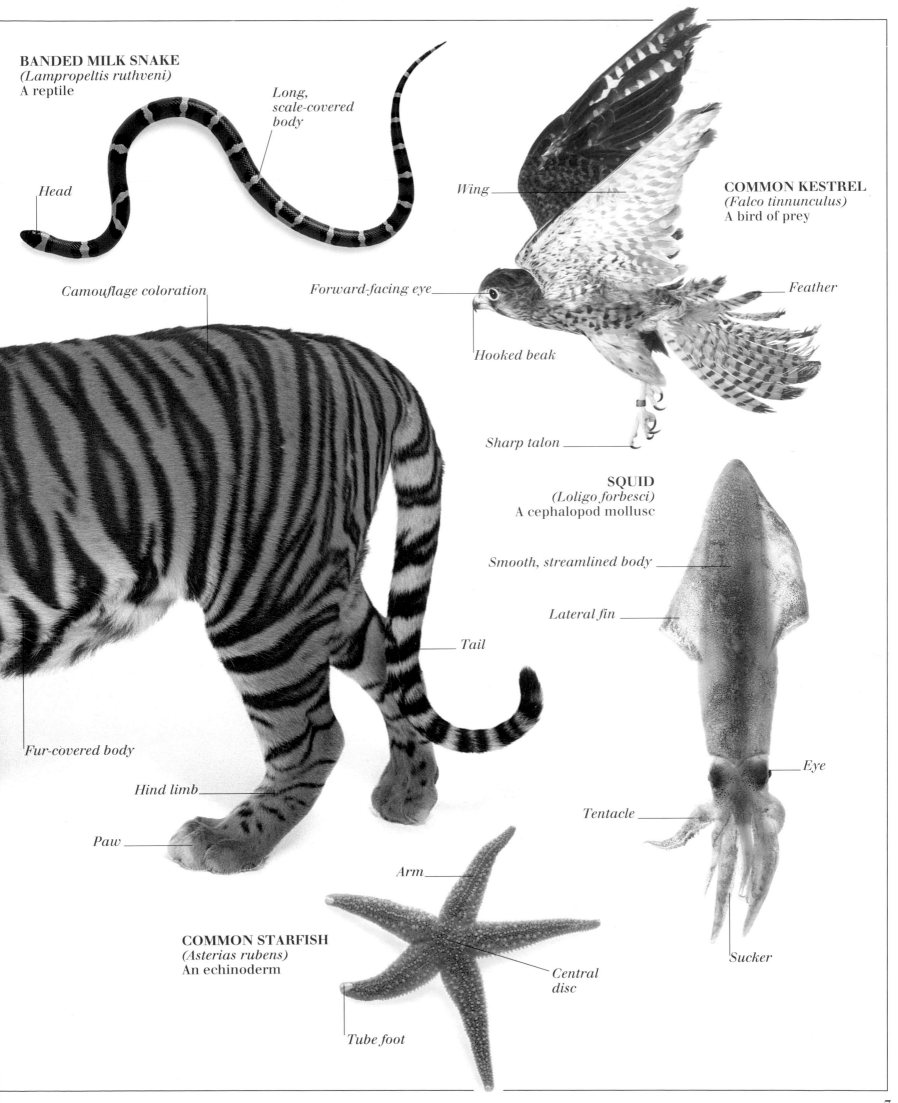

BANDED MILK SNAKE
(Lampropeltis ruthveni)
A reptile

*Long,
scale-covered
body*

Head

Camouflage coloration

COMMON KESTREL
(Falco tinnunculus)
A bird of prey

Wing

Forward-facing eye

Feather

Hooked beak

Sharp talon

SQUID
(Loligo forbesci)
A cephalopod mollusc

Smooth, streamlined body

Lateral fin

Tail

Fur-covered body

Hind limb

Paw

Eye

Tentacle

Arm

COMMON STARFISH
(Asterias rubens)
An echinoderm

*Central
disc*

Sucker

Tube foot

Animal heads

MOST ACTIVELY MOVING ANIMALS HAVE a definite head region at the front of their bodies. The head is usually the first part of an animal to receive information from the surroundings, and it therefore has several specialized sensory structures—eyes, ears, whiskers, and antennae, for example—to detect any changes in its surroundings. To enable the animal to react appropriately to external changes, sensory information is processed by the brain, which is located inside the head. In most higher animals, the head also has a mouth and a pair of nostrils. The mouth—and the teeth, if the animal has them—is used to capture and ingest food; it also contains taste buds to detect chemicals, and can be used for breathing. Similarly, the nostrils are used for breathing, and sensory structures in the nasal cavity detect odours.

PUFF ADDER
(Bitis arietans)
A reptile

Eye

Nostril

Sensory forked tongue

BLUE-STREAKED LORY
(Eos reticulata)
A seed- and fruit-eating bird

Eye

Nostril

Hook of beak for extracting fruit pulp

Broad base of beak for cracking seeds

FEMALE GOLIATH BEETLE
(Goliathus meleagris)
An insect

Front leg

Compound eye

BLUE-SPOTTED SEA BREAM
(Pagrus coerulostictus)
A bony fish

Spine of dorsal fin

Eye

Mouth

Preoperculum

Pectoral fin

Operculum (gill cover)

Pelvic fin

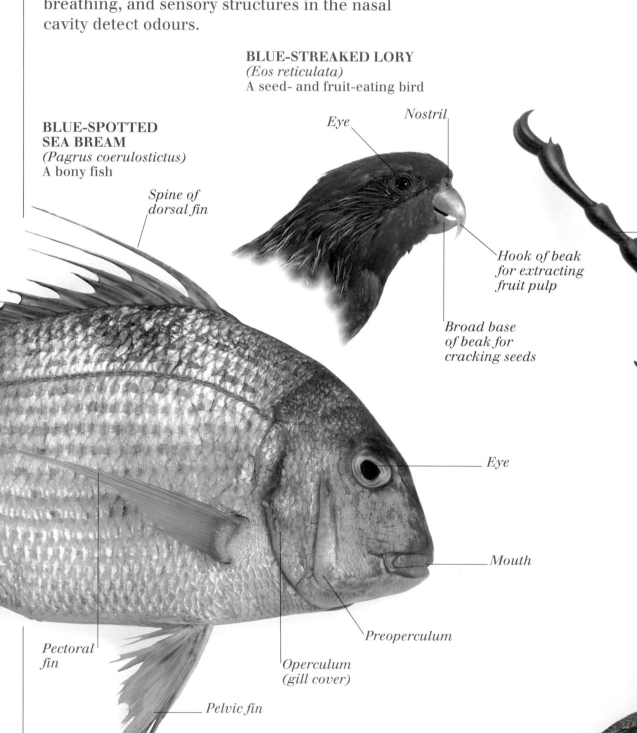

8

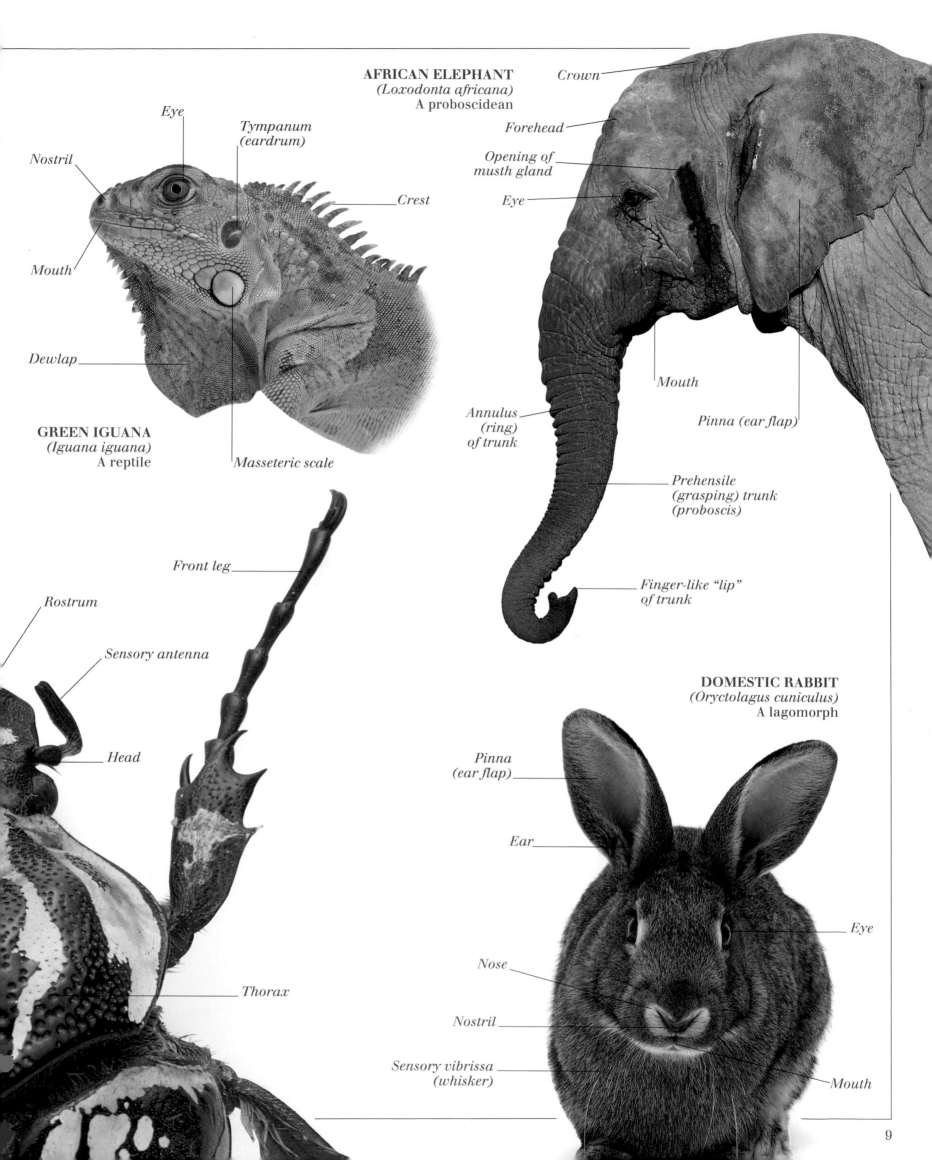

GREEN IGUANA
(Iguana iguana)
A reptile

Eye

Tympanum
(eardrum)

Nostril

Crest

Mouth

Dewlap

Masseteric scale

AFRICAN ELEPHANT
(Loxodonta africana)
A proboscidean

Crown

Forehead

Opening of
musth gland

Eye

Mouth

Annulus
(ring)
of trunk

Pinna *(ear flap)*

Prehensile
(grasping) trunk
(proboscis)

Finger-like "lip"
of trunk

Front leg

Rostrum

Sensory antenna

Head

Thorax

DOMESTIC RABBIT
(Oryctolagus cuniculus)
A lagomorph

Pinna
(ear flap)

Ear

Eye

Nose

Nostril

Sensory vibrissa
(whisker)

Mouth

9

Butterflies and moths

BUTTERFLIES AND MOTHS FORM THE order Lepidoptera, one of the divisions of the large class Insecta, which is itself part of the even larger phylum Arthropoda. Lepidopterans are one of the biggest groups of insects, with about 150,000 species (about 15 per cent of all known insects). They are characterized by having wings covered with tiny scales, hence the name of their order (Lepidoptera means "scale wings"). Butterflies and moths also possess features that are common to all insects: an exoskeleton (external skeleton); three pairs of jointed legs, although the front pair are very small in some lepidopterans; three body sections (head, thorax, and abdomen); and one pair of sensory antennae. Like certain other insects (beetles, flies, and bees, for example), butterflies and moths undergo complete metamorphosis during their life-cycle.

DIFFERENCES BETWEEN BUTTERFLIES AND MOTHS

The separation of lepidopterans into butterflies and moths is largely artificial as there are no features that categorically distinguish one group from the other. In general, however, most butterflies fly by day, whereas most moths are night-flyers; butterflies tend to have clubbed antennae, whereas those of moths tend to be plain or feathery; butterflies usually rest with their wings upright over their backs, whereas moths rest with their wings flat; and butterflies tend to be more brightly coloured than moths.

EXTERNAL FEATURES OF A BUTTERFLY

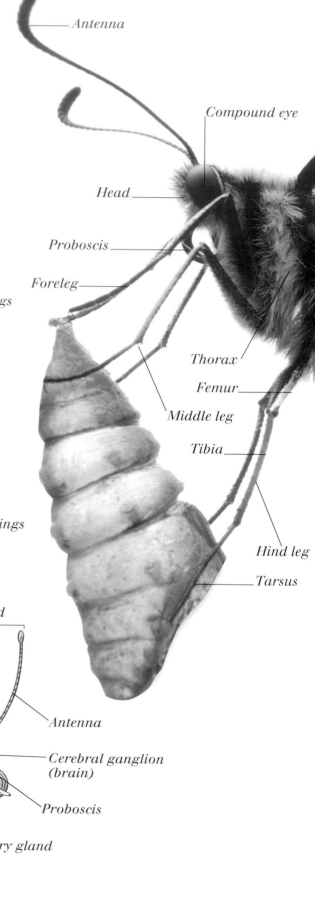

- Antenna
- Compound eye
- Head
- Proboscis
- Foreleg
- Thorax
- Femur
- Middle leg
- Tibia
- Hind leg
- Tarsus

MOTH

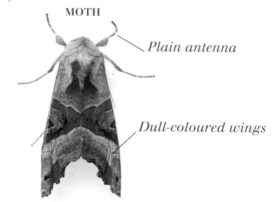

- Plain antenna
- Dull-coloured wings

BUTTERFLY

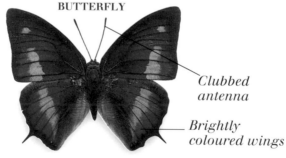

- Clubbed antenna
- Brightly coloured wings

INTERNAL ANATOMY OF A FEMALE BUTTERFLY

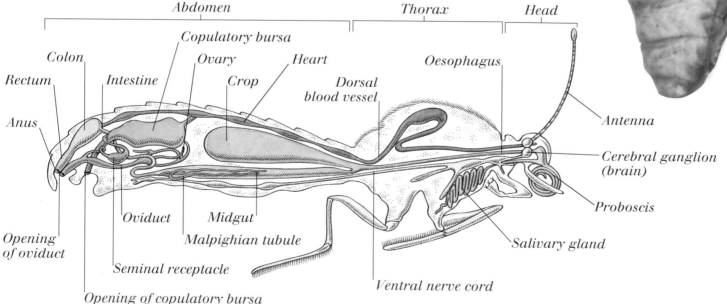

- Abdomen
- Thorax
- Head
- Copulatory bursa
- Colon
- Ovary
- Heart
- Oesophagus
- Rectum
- Intestine
- Crop
- Dorsal blood vessel
- Anus
- Antenna
- Cerebral ganglion (brain)
- Proboscis
- Oviduct
- Midgut
- Salivary gland
- Opening of oviduct
- Malpighian tubule
- Seminal receptacle
- Ventral nerve cord
- Opening of copulatory bursa

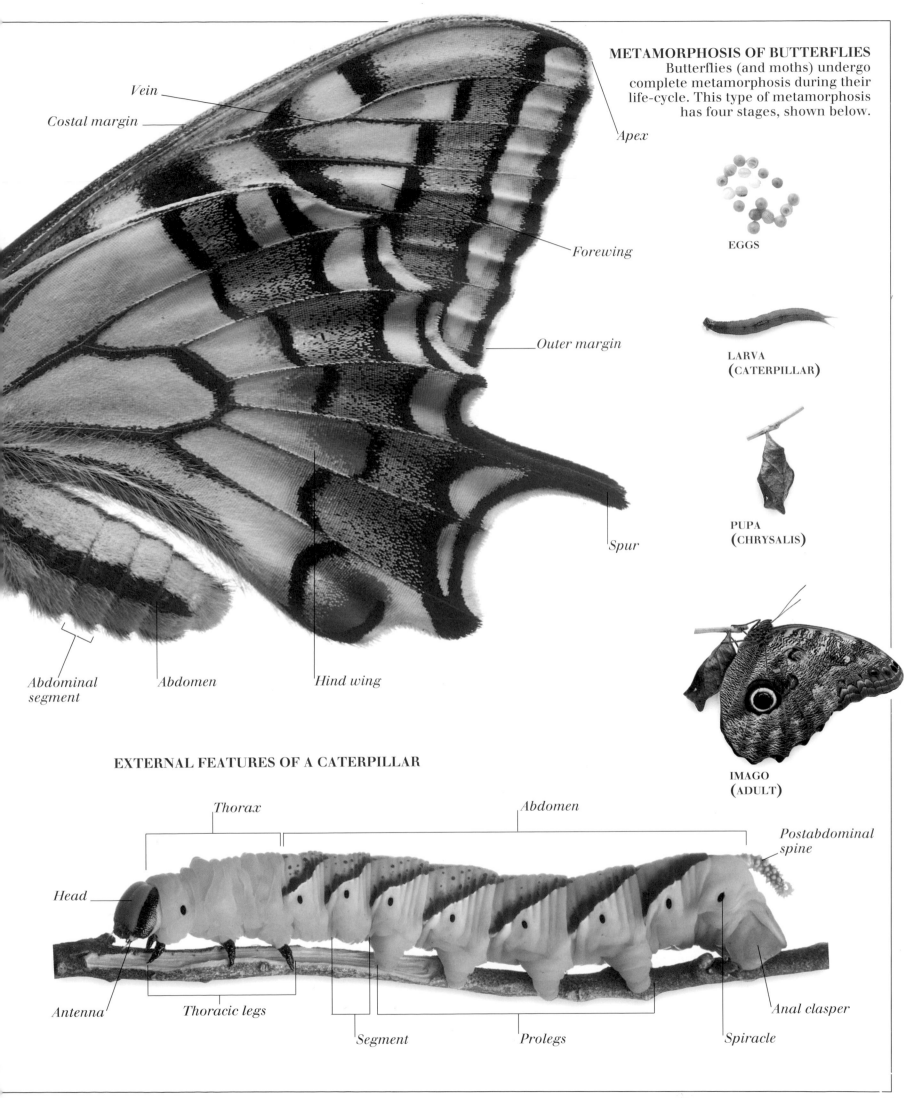

Vein

Costal margin

Apex

Forewing

Outer margin

Spur

Abdominal segment

Abdomen

Hind wing

METAMORPHOSIS OF BUTTERFLIES
Butterflies (and moths) undergo complete metamorphosis during their life-cycle. This type of metamorphosis has four stages, shown below.

EGGS

LARVA
(CATERPILLAR)

PUPA
(CHRYSALIS)

IMAGO
(ADULT)

EXTERNAL FEATURES OF A CATERPILLAR

Thorax

Abdomen

Postabdominal spine

Head

Antenna

Thoracic legs

Segment

Prolegs

Anal clasper

Spiracle

Beetles, ants, and bees

BEETLES, ANTS, AND BEES BELONG to different orders in the class Insecta, which is a division of the phylum Arthropoda. Beetles (order Coleoptera) are the biggest group of insects, with about 300,000 species. The characteristic feature of beetles is a pair of hard elytra (wing cases), which are modified front wings. The principal function of the elytra is to protect the hind wings, which are used for flying. Ants, together with bees and wasps, form the order Hymenoptera, which contains about 200,000 species. This group is characterized by a marked narrowing between the thorax and abdomen. Both of the above groups also have features common to all insects: an exoskeleton (external skeleton); three pairs of jointed legs; three body sections (head, thorax, and abdomen); and one pair of sensory antennae.

TYPES OF BEES

Some bees (bumblebees and honeybees, for example) exhibit polymorphism, that is, different types (or castes) of bees occur in the same species. Bumblebees have three castes: workers, which are sterile females; drones, which are fertile males; and queens, which are fertile females.

QUEEN BUMBLEBEE

DRONE BUMBLEBEE

WORKER BUMBLEBEE

EXTERNAL FEATURES OF A BUMBLEBEE

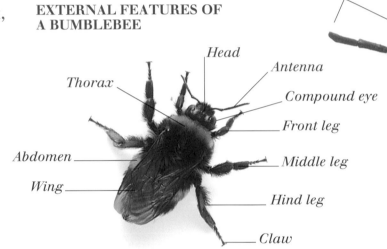

Head

Antenna

Thorax

Compound eye

Front leg

Abdomen

Middle leg

Wing

Hind leg

Claw

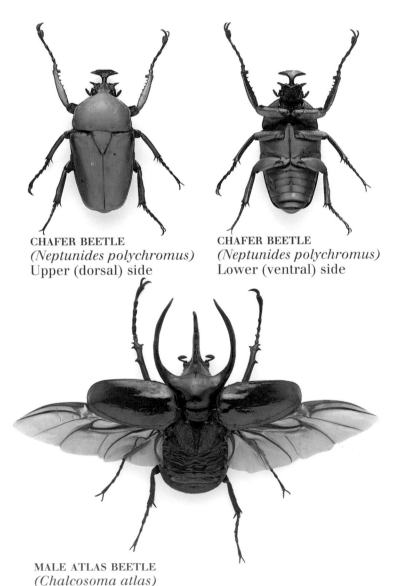

CHAFER BEETLE
(Neptunides polychromus)
Upper (dorsal) side

CHAFER BEETLE
(Neptunides polychromus)
Lower (ventral) side

EXAMPLES OF BEETLES

MALE ATLAS BEETLE
(Chalcosoma atlas)

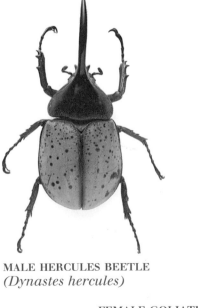

MALE HERCULES BEETLE
(Dynastes hercules)

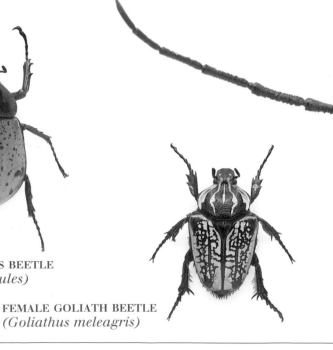

FEMALE GOLIATH BEETLE
(Goliathus meleagris)

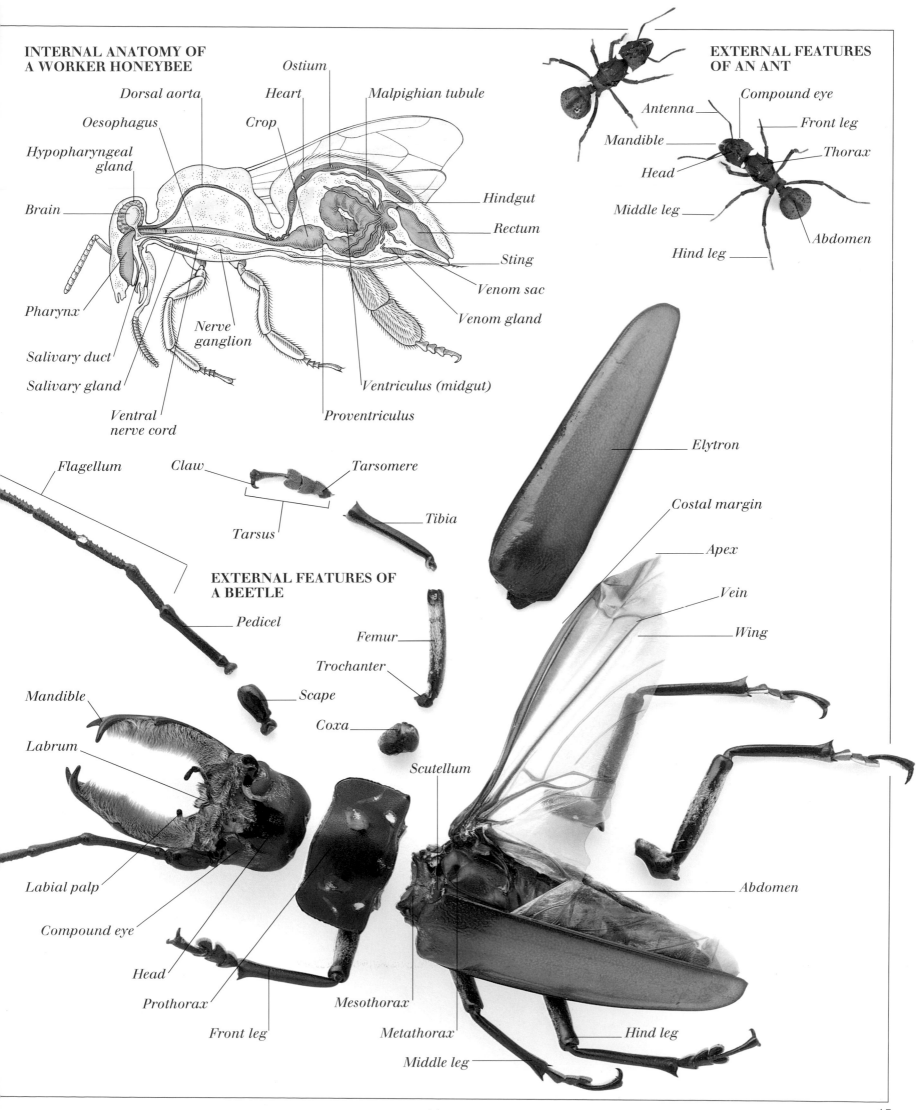

INTERNAL ANATOMY OF A WORKER HONEYBEE

Ostium

Dorsal aorta

Heart

Malpighian tubule

Oesophagus

Crop

Hypopharyngeal gland

Brain

Hindgut

Rectum

Pharynx

Sting

Venom sac

Nerve ganglion

Venom gland

Salivary duct

Salivary gland

Ventriculus (midgut)

Ventral nerve cord

Proventriculus

EXTERNAL FEATURES OF AN ANT

Antenna

Compound eye

Front leg

Mandible

Thorax

Head

Middle leg

Abdomen

Hind leg

Flagellum

Claw

Tarsomere

Tibia

Tarsus

Elytron

Costal margin

EXTERNAL FEATURES OF A BEETLE

Apex

Vein

Pedicel

Femur

Wing

Trochanter

Mandible

Scape

Labrum

Coxa

Scutellum

Compound eye

Abdomen

Head

Labial palp

Prothorax

Front leg

Mesothorax

Metathorax

Hind leg

Middle leg

13

Arachnids

THE CLASS ARACHNIDA INCLUDES SPIDERS (order Araneae) and scorpions (order Scorpiones). The class is part of the phylum Arthropoda, which also includes insects and crustaceans. Spiders and scorpions are characterized by having four pairs of walking legs; a pair of pincer-like mouthparts called chelicerae; another pair of frontal appendages called pedipalps, which are sensory in spiders but used for grasping in scorpions; and a body divided into two sections (a combined head and thorax called a cephalothorax or prosoma, and an abdomen or opisthosoma). Unlike other arthropods, spiders and scorpions lack antennae. Spiders and scorpions are carnivorous. Spiders poison prey by biting with the fanged chelicerae, scorpions by stinging with the end of the metasoma (tail).

MEXICAN TRUE RED-LEGGED TARANTULA
(Euathlus emilia)

INTERNAL ANATOMY OF A FEMALE SPIDER

EXTERNAL FEATURES OF A SCORPION

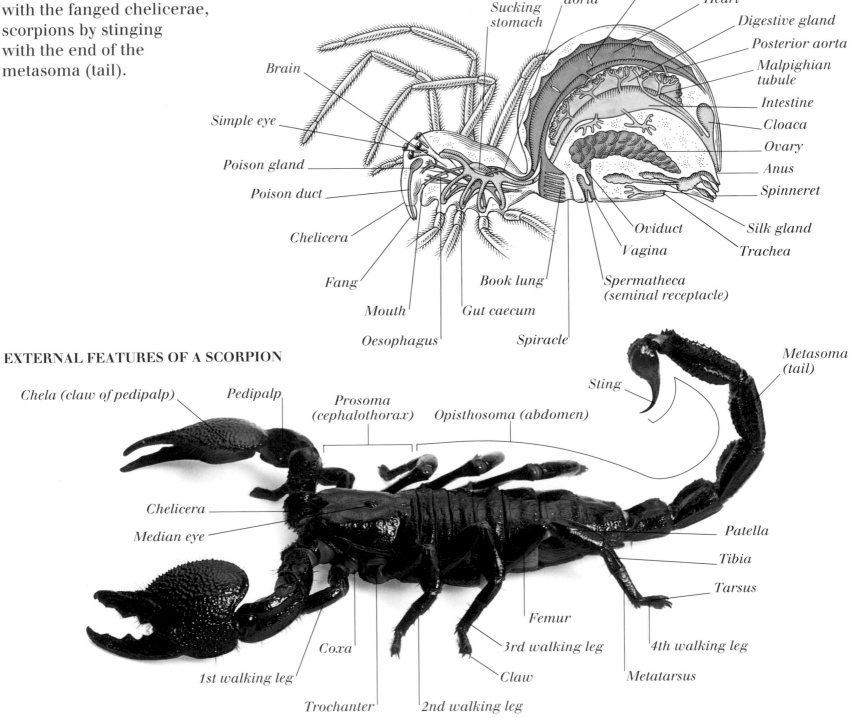

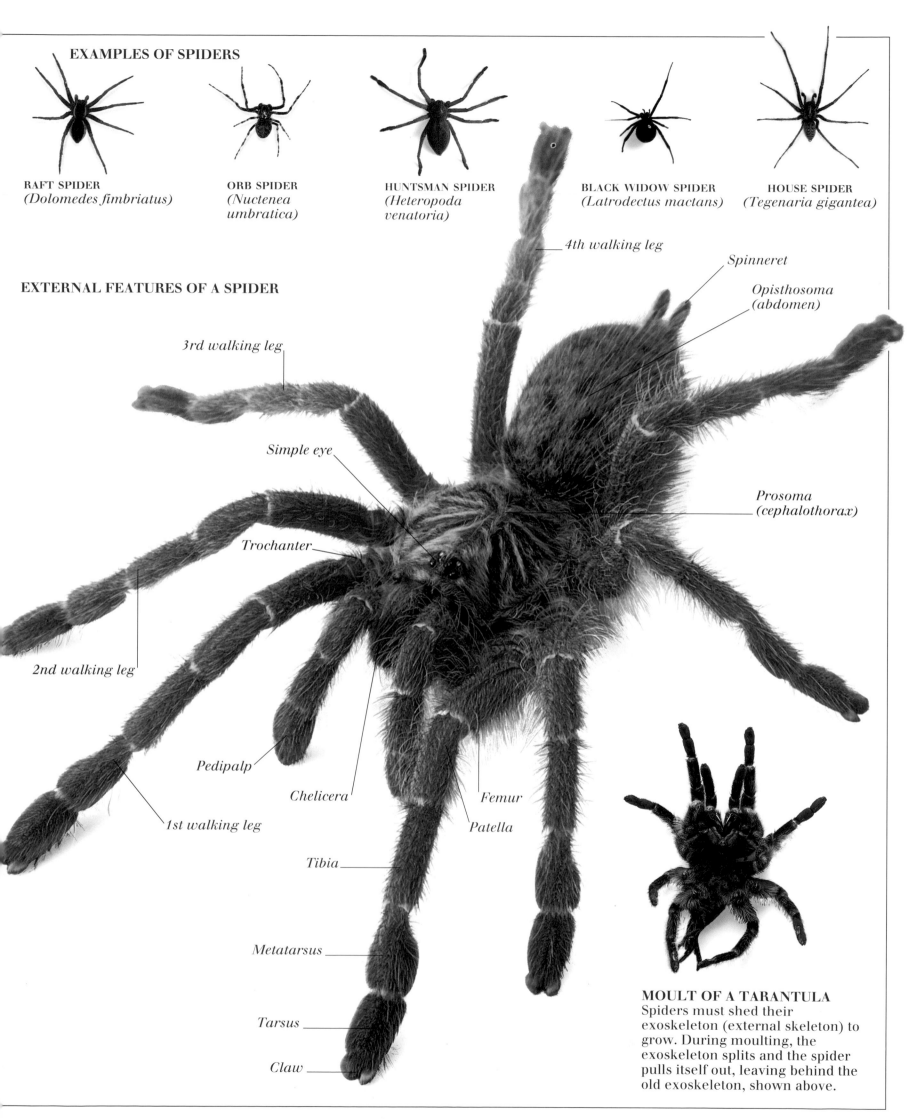

EXAMPLES OF SPIDERS

RAFT SPIDER
(Dolomedes fimbriatus)

ORB SPIDER
(Nuctenea umbratica)

HUNTSMAN SPIDER
(Heteropoda venatoria)

BLACK WIDOW SPIDER
(Latrodectus mactans)

HOUSE SPIDER
(Tegenaria gigantea)

EXTERNAL FEATURES OF A SPIDER

4th walking leg

Spinneret

Opisthosoma (abdomen)

3rd walking leg

Simple eye

Prosoma (cephalothorax)

Trochanter

2nd walking leg

Pedipalp

Chelicera

Femur

Patella

1st walking leg

Tibia

Metatarsus

Tarsus

Claw

MOULT OF A TARANTULA
Spiders must shed their exoskeleton (external skeleton) to grow. During moulting, the exoskeleton splits and the spider pulls itself out, leaving behind the old exoskeleton, shown above.

15

Worms, flukes, and leeches

THE TERM "WORM" HAS NO STRICT SCIENTIFIC meaning, but it is commonly applied to various long, thin, soft-bodied animals. Probably the best-known groups of worms are the segmented worms (phylum Annelida), which include earthworms, marine worms such as sandworms and ragworms, and also leeches; and the flatworms (phylum Platyhelminthes), which include tapeworms and flukes. Annelid worms have cylindrical bodies divided into many segments; a coelom (body cavity) around the gut; and relatively well-developed nervous, circulatory, and other body systems. Platyhelminths have flattened, unsegmented bodies; no coelom; and comparatively simple body systems. Many platyhelminths are parasites. For example, the liver fluke infests cattle and sheep, whereas the pork tapeworm and blood fluke infect humans, in whom they cause disease.

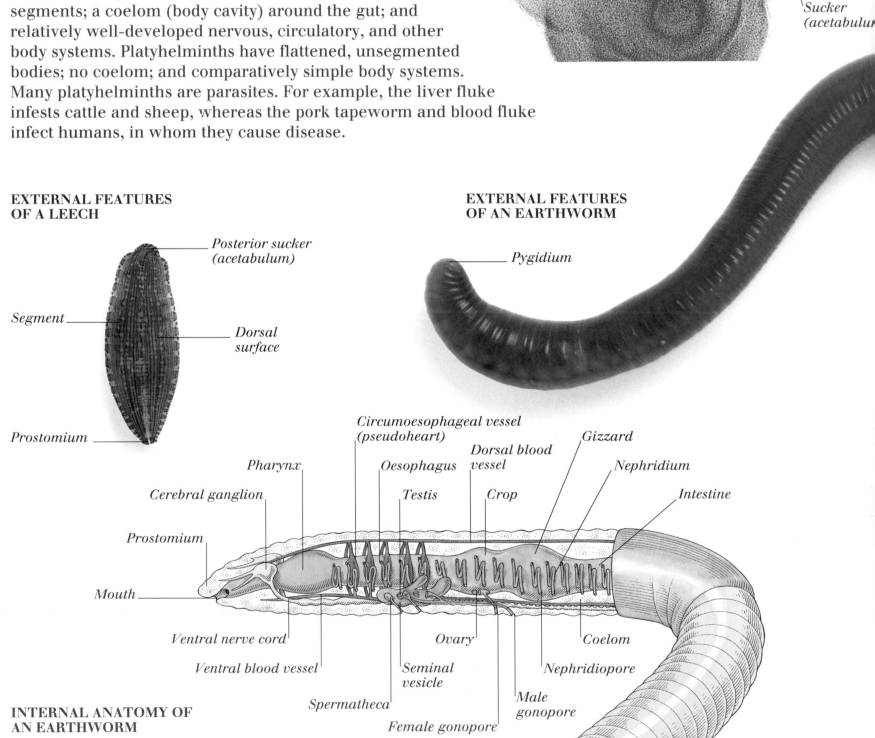

HEAD (SCOLEX) OF A PORK TAPEWORM

Rostellum

Hook

Sucker (acetabulum)

EXTERNAL FEATURES OF A LEECH

Posterior sucker (acetabulum)

Segment

Dorsal surface

Prostomium

EXTERNAL FEATURES OF AN EARTHWORM

Pygidium

Circumoesophageal vessel (pseudoheart)

Pharynx

Oesophagus

Dorsal blood vessel

Gizzard

Cerebral ganglion

Testis

Crop

Nephridium

Prostomium

Intestine

Mouth

Ventral nerve cord

Ovary

Coelom

Ventral blood vessel

Seminal vesicle

Nephridiopore

Spermatheca

Male gonopore

INTERNAL ANATOMY OF AN EARTHWORM

Female gonopore

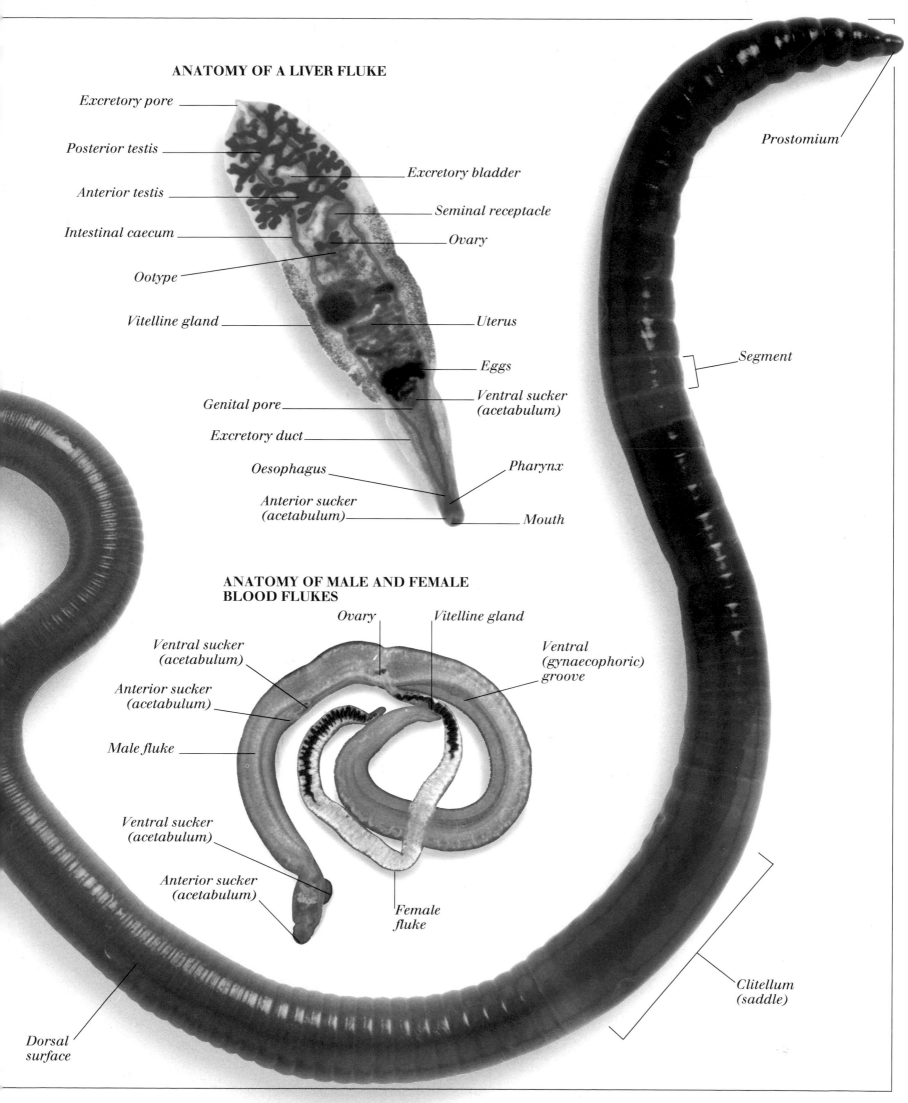

ANATOMY OF A LIVER FLUKE

Excretory pore

Posterior testis

Excretory bladder

Anterior testis

Seminal receptacle

Intestinal caecum

Ovary

Ootype

Vitelline gland

Uterus

Eggs

Genital pore

Ventral sucker
(acetabulum)

Excretory duct

Oesophagus

Pharynx

Anterior sucker
(acetabulum)

Mouth

**ANATOMY OF MALE AND FEMALE
BLOOD FLUKES**

Ovary

Vitelline gland

Ventral sucker
(acetabulum)

Ventral
(gynaecophoric)
groove

Anterior sucker
(acetabulum)

Male fluke

Ventral sucker
(acetabulum)

Anterior sucker
(acetabulum)

Female
fluke

Prostomium

Segment

Clitellum
(saddle)

Dorsal
surface

17

Sharks and jawless fish

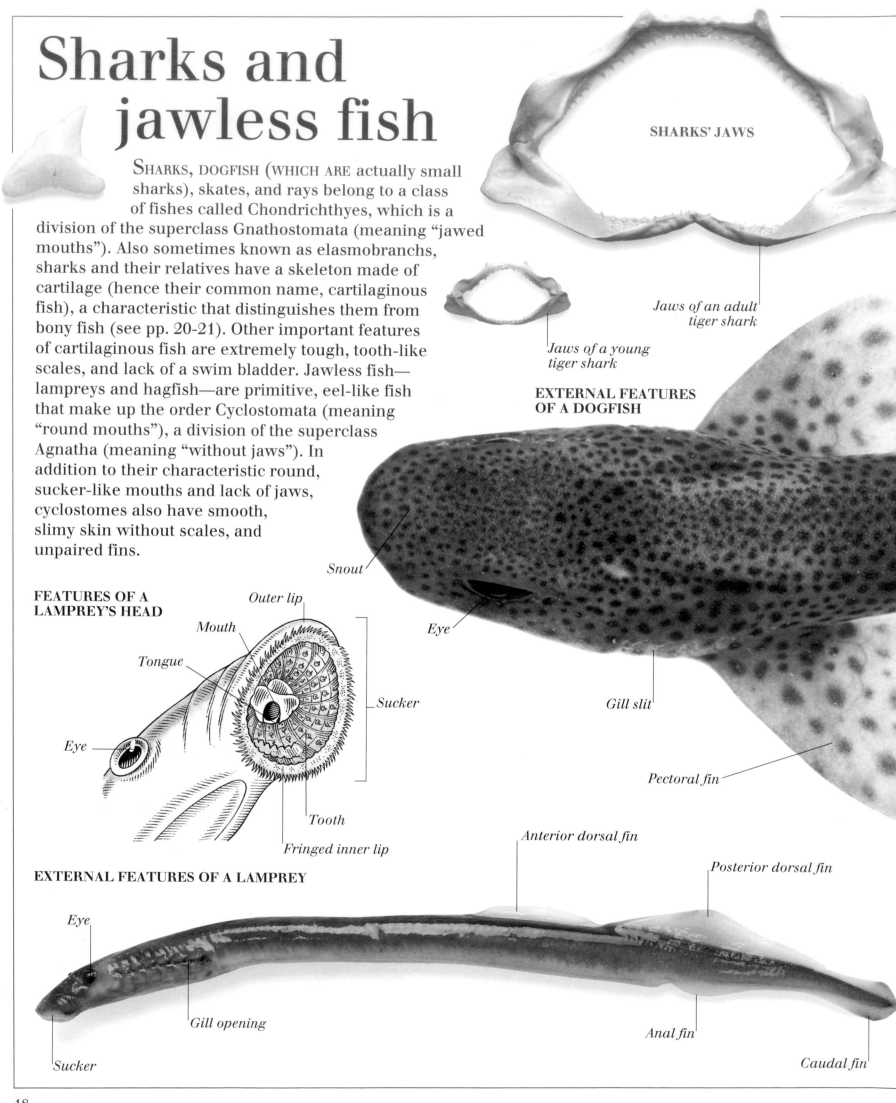

SHARKS, DOGFISH (WHICH ARE actually small sharks), skates, and rays belong to a class of fishes called Chondrichthyes, which is a division of the superclass Gnathostomata (meaning "jawed mouths"). Also sometimes known as elasmobranchs, sharks and their relatives have a skeleton made of cartilage (hence their common name, cartilaginous fish), a characteristic that distinguishes them from bony fish (see pp. 20-21). Other important features of cartilaginous fish are extremely tough, tooth-like scales, and lack of a swim bladder. Jawless fish—lampreys and hagfish—are primitive, eel-like fish that make up the order Cyclostomata (meaning "round mouths"), a division of the superclass Agnatha (meaning "without jaws"). In addition to their characteristic round, sucker-like mouths and lack of jaws, cyclostomes also have smooth, slimy skin without scales, and unpaired fins.

SHARKS' JAWS

Jaws of an adult tiger shark

Jaws of a young tiger shark

EXTERNAL FEATURES OF A DOGFISH

Snout

Eye

Gill slit

Pectoral fin

FEATURES OF A LAMPREY'S HEAD

Outer lip

Mouth

Tongue

Sucker

Eye

Tooth

Fringed inner lip

EXTERNAL FEATURES OF A LAMPREY

Eye

Gill opening

Sucker

Anterior dorsal fin

Posterior dorsal fin

Anal fin

Caudal fin

EXAMPLES OF CARTILAGINOUS FISH

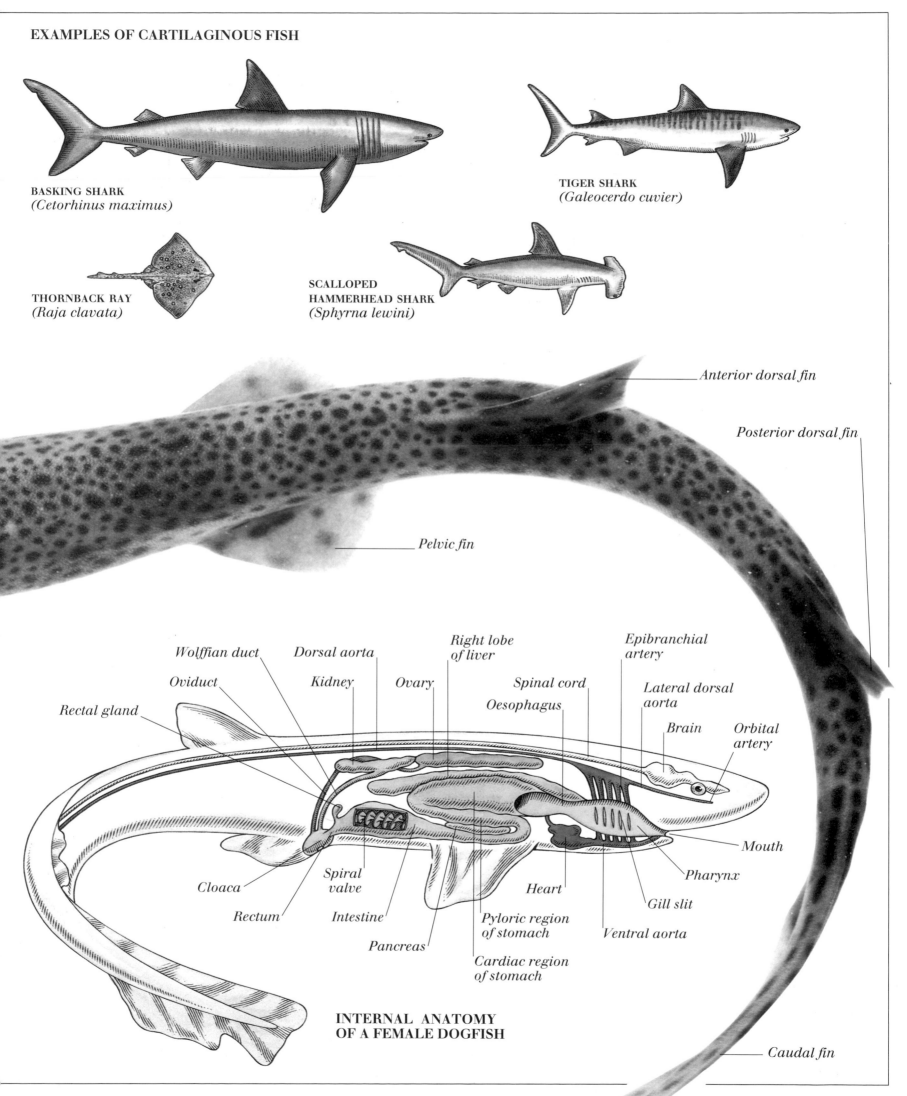

BASKING SHARK
(Cetorhinus maximus)

TIGER SHARK
(Galeocerdo cuvier)

THORNBACK RAY
(Raja clavata)

**SCALLOPED
HAMMERHEAD SHARK**
(Sphyrna lewini)

Anterior dorsal fin

Posterior dorsal fin

Pelvic fin

Wolffian duct

Dorsal aorta

Right lobe
of liver

Epibranchial
artery

Oviduct

Kidney

Ovary

Spinal cord

Lateral dorsal
aorta

Rectal gland

Oesophagus

Brain

Orbital
artery

Mouth

Cloaca

Pharynx

Spiral
valve

Heart

Gill slit

Rectum

Intestine

Ventral aorta

Pancreas

Pyloric region
of stomach

Cardiac region
of stomach

**INTERNAL ANATOMY
OF A FEMALE DOGFISH**

Caudal fin

19

Bony fish

BONY FISH, SUCH AS CARP, TROUT, SALMON, perch, and cod, are by far the best known and largest group of fish, with more than 20,000 species (over 95 per cent of all known fish). As their name suggests, bony fish have skeletons made of bone, in contrast to the cartilaginous skeletons of sharks, jawless fish, and their relatives (see pp. 18-19). Other typical features of bony fish include a swim bladder, which functions as a variable-buoyancy organ, enabling a fish to remain effortlessly at whatever depth it is swimming; relatively thin, bone-like scales; a flap (called an operculum) covering the gills; and paired pelvic and pectoral fins. Scientifically, bony fish belong to the class Osteichthyes, which is a division of the superclass Gnathostomata (meaning "jawed mouths").

HOW FISH BREATHE
Fish "breathe" by extracting oxygen from water through their gills. Water is sucked in through the mouth; simultaneously, the opercula close to prevent the water from escaping. The mouth is then closed, and muscles in the walls of the mouth, pharynx, and opercular cavity contract to pump the water inside over the gills and out through the opercula. Some fish rely on swimming with their mouths open to keep water flowing over the gills.

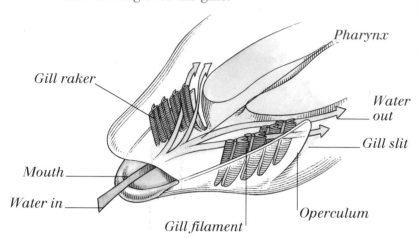

Gill raker

Pharynx

Water out

Gill slit

Mouth

Water in

Gill filament

Operculum

EXAMPLES OF BONY FISH

MANDARINFISH
(Synchiropus splendidus)

ANGLERFISH
(Caulophryne jordani)

OCEANIC SEAHORSE
(Hippocampus kuda)

LIONFISH
(Pterois volitans)

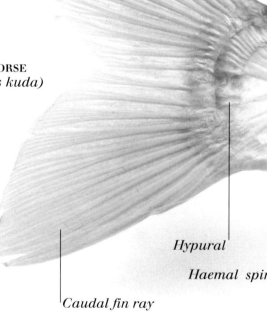
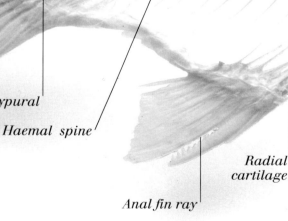

Vertebra

Neural spine

Hypural

Haemal spine

Caudal fin ray

Anal fin ray

Radial cartilage

STURGEON
(Acipenser sturio)

SNOWFLAKE MORAY EEL
(Echidna nebulosa)

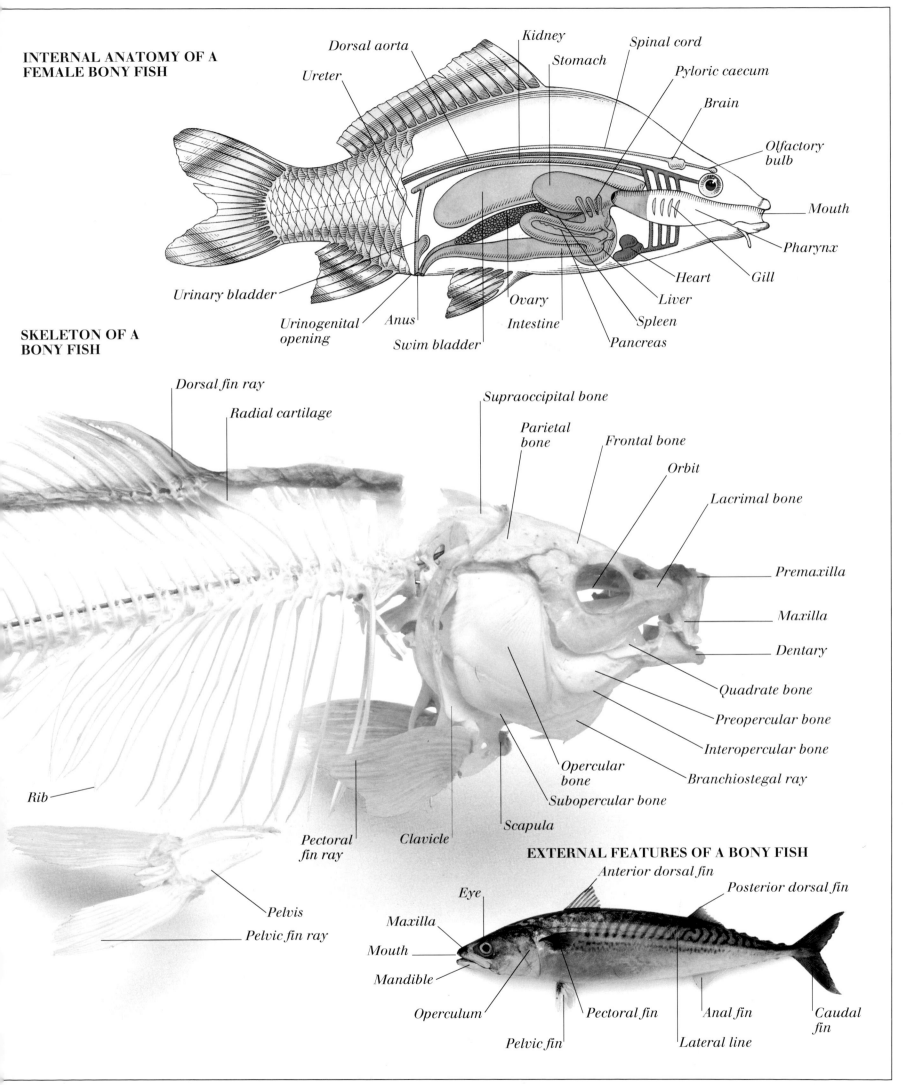

INTERNAL ANATOMY OF A FEMALE BONY FISH

Kidney

Dorsal aorta

Stomach

Spinal cord

Pyloric caecum

Ureter

Brain

Olfactory bulb

Mouth

Pharynx

Urinary bladder

Gill

Heart

Urinogenital opening

Anus

Ovary

Intestine

Spleen

Liver

Swim bladder

Pancreas

SKELETON OF A BONY FISH

Dorsal fin ray

Radial cartilage

Supraoccipital bone

Parietal bone

Frontal bone

Orbit

Lacrimal bone

Premaxilla

Maxilla

Dentary

Quadrate bone

Preopercular bone

Interopercular bone

Branchiostegal ray

Opercular bone

Subopercular bone

Scapula

Rib

Pectoral fin ray

Clavicle

Pelvis

Pelvic fin ray

EXTERNAL FEATURES OF A BONY FISH

Anterior dorsal fin

Posterior dorsal fin

Eye

Maxilla

Mouth

Mandible

Operculum

Pectoral fin

Anal fin

Caudal fin

Pelvic fin

Lateral line

Starfish and sea urchins

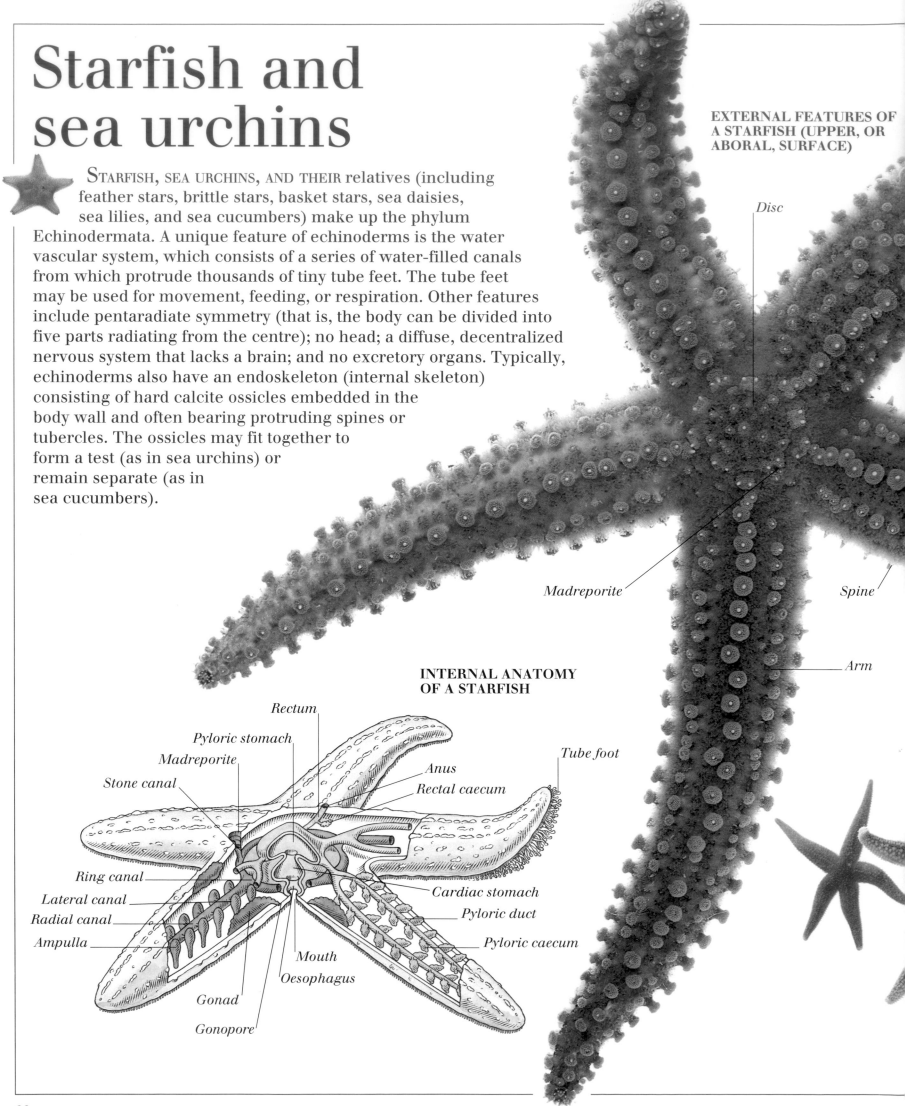

STARFISH, SEA URCHINS, AND THEIR relatives (including feather stars, brittle stars, basket stars, sea daisies, sea lilies, and sea cucumbers) make up the phylum Echinodermata. A unique feature of echinoderms is the water vascular system, which consists of a series of water-filled canals from which protrude thousands of tiny tube feet. The tube feet may be used for movement, feeding, or respiration. Other features include pentaradiate symmetry (that is, the body can be divided into five parts radiating from the centre); no head; a diffuse, decentralized nervous system that lacks a brain; and no excretory organs. Typically, echinoderms also have an endoskeleton (internal skeleton) consisting of hard calcite ossicles embedded in the body wall and often bearing protruding spines or tubercles. The ossicles may fit together to form a test (as in sea urchins) or remain separate (as in sea cucumbers).

EXTERNAL FEATURES OF A STARFISH (UPPER, OR ABORAL, SURFACE)

Disc

Madreporite

Spine

Arm

INTERNAL ANATOMY OF A STARFISH

Rectum

Pyloric stomach

Madreporite

Stone canal

Anus

Rectal caecum

Tube foot

Ring canal

Lateral canal

Radial canal

Ampulla

Cardiac stomach

Pyloric duct

Pyloric caecum

Mouth

Oesophagus

Gonad

Gonopore

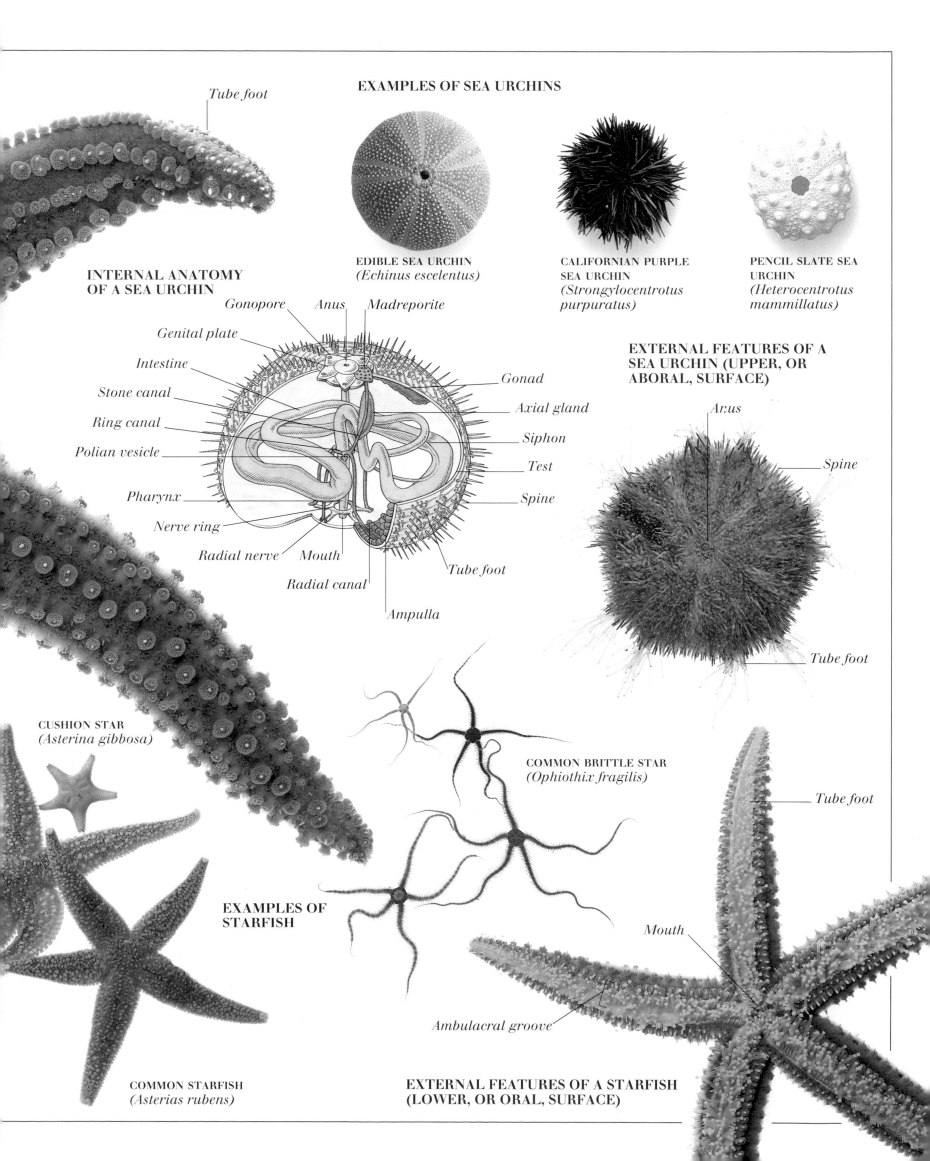

Tube foot

EXAMPLES OF SEA URCHINS

EDIBLE SEA URCHIN
(*Echinus escelentus*)

CALIFORNIAN PURPLE SEA URCHIN
(*Strongylocentrotus purpuratus*)

PENCIL SLATE SEA URCHIN
(*Heterocentrotus mammillatus*)

INTERNAL ANATOMY OF A SEA URCHIN

Gonopore
Anus
Madreporite
Genital plate
Intestine
Gonad
Stone canal
Axial gland
Ring canal
Siphon
Polian vesicle
Test
Pharynx
Spine
Nerve ring
Radial nerve
Mouth
Tube foot
Radial canal
Ampulla

EXTERNAL FEATURES OF A SEA URCHIN (UPPER, OR ABORAL, SURFACE)

Anus
Spine
Tube foot

CUSHION STAR
(*Asterina gibbosa*)

COMMON BRITTLE STAR
(*Ophiothix fragilis*)

Tube foot

EXAMPLES OF STARFISH

Mouth

Ambulacral groove

COMMON STARFISH
(*Asterias rubens*)

EXTERNAL FEATURES OF A STARFISH (LOWER, OR ORAL, SURFACE)

Sponges, jellyfish, and sea anemones

SPONGES ARE MAINLY MARINE animals that make up the phylum Porifera. They are among the simplest of all animals, having no tissues or organs. Their bodies consist of two layers of cells separated by a jelly-like layer (mesohyal) that is strengthened by mineral spicules or protein fibres. The body is perforated by a system of pores and water channels called the aquiferous system. Special cells (choanocytes) with whip-like structures (flagella) draw water through the aquiferous system, thereby bringing tiny food particles to the sponge's cells. Jellyfish (class Scyphozoa), sea anemones (class Anthozoa), and corals (also class Anthozoa) belong to the phylum Cnidaria, also known as Coelenterata. More complex than sponges, coelenterates have simple tissues, such as nervous tissue; a radially symmetrical body; and a mouth surrounded by tentacles with unique stinging cells (cnidocytes).

INTERNAL ANATOMY OF A SPONGE

Amoebocyte

Osculum (excurrent pore)

Choanocyte (collar cell)

Ostium (incurrent pore)

Porocyte (pore cell)

Mesohyal

Spongocoel (atrium; paragaster)

Spicule

Pinacocyte (epidermal cell)

Ostium (incurrent pore)

SKELETON OF A SPONGE

Protein matrix

Pore

EXTERNAL FEATURES OF A SEA ANEMONE

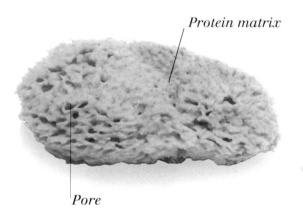

Tentacle

EXAMPLES OF SEA ANEMONES

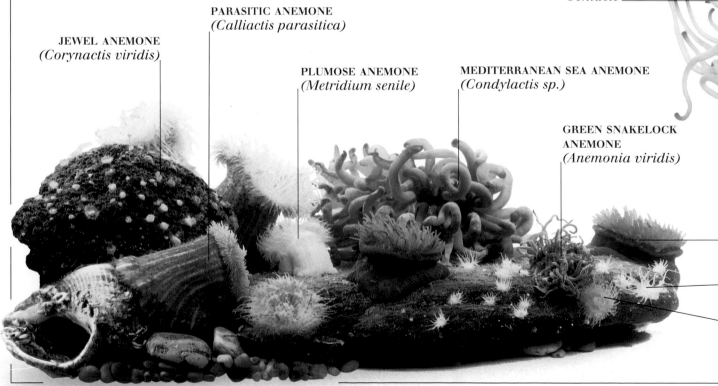

JEWEL ANEMONE
(Corynactis viridis)

PARASITIC ANEMONE
(Calliactis parasitica)

PLUMOSE ANEMONE
(Metridium senile)

MEDITERRANEAN SEA ANEMONE
(Condylactis sp.)

GREEN SNAKELOCK ANEMONE
(Anemonia viridis)

BEADLET ANEMONE
(Actinia equina)

GHOST ANEMONE
(Actinothoe sphyrodeta)

Sagartia elegans

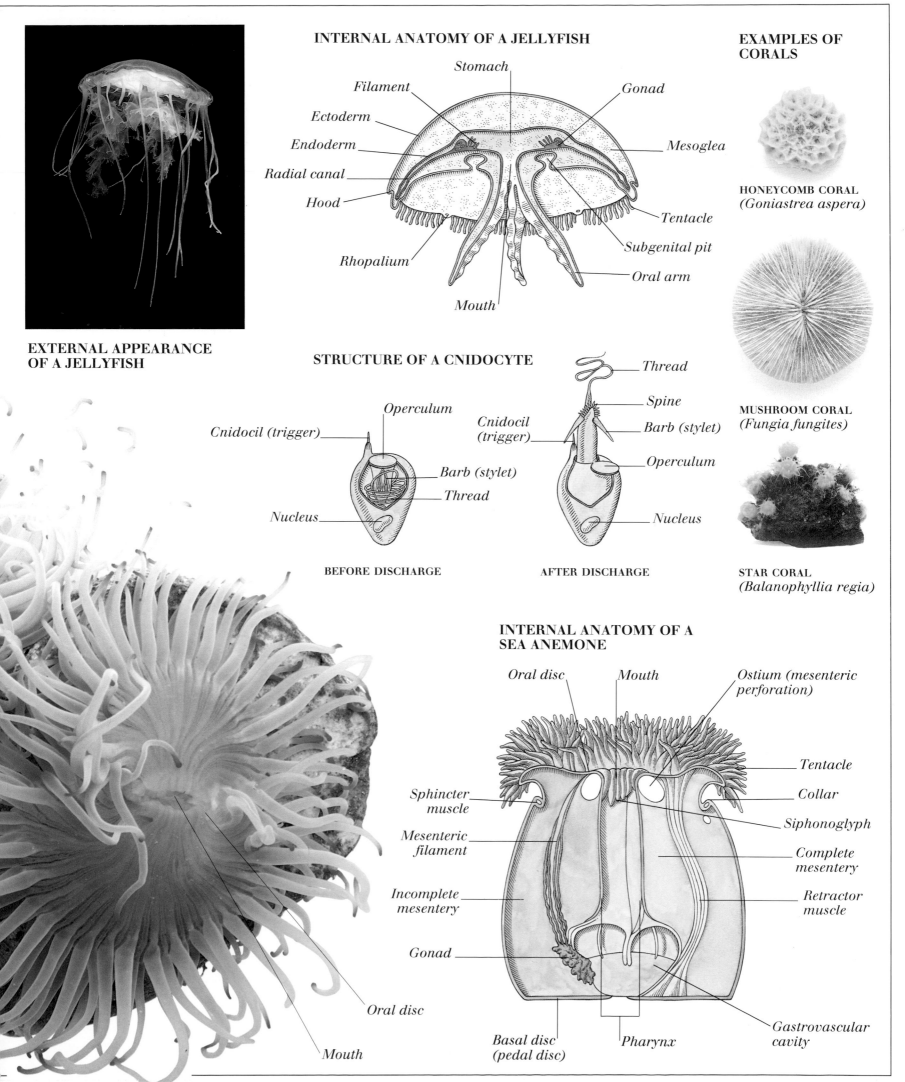

**EXTERNAL APPEARANCE
OF A JELLYFISH**

INTERNAL ANATOMY OF A JELLYFISH

Stomach

Filament

Gonad

Ectoderm

Endoderm

Mesoglea

Radial canal

Hood

Tentacle

Subgenital pit

Rhopalium

Oral arm

Mouth

**EXAMPLES OF
CORALS**

HONEYCOMB CORAL
(*Goniastrea aspera*)

MUSHROOM CORAL
(*Fungia fungites*)

STRUCTURE OF A CNIDOCYTE

Operculum

Thread

Cnidocil (trigger)

Spine

Cnidocil
(trigger)

Barb (stylet)

Barb (stylet)

Operculum

Thread

Nucleus

Nucleus

BEFORE DISCHARGE

AFTER DISCHARGE

STAR CORAL
(*Balanophyllia regia*)

**INTERNAL ANATOMY OF A
SEA ANEMONE**

Oral disc

Mouth

Ostium (mesenteric
perforation)

Sphincter
muscle

Tentacle

Collar

Siphonoglyph

Mesenteric
filament

Complete
mesentery

Incomplete
mesentery

Retractor
muscle

Gonad

Oral disc

Gastrovascular
cavity

Mouth

Basal disc
(pedal disc)

Pharynx

Molluscs

THE PHYLUM MOLLUSCA (MOLLUSCS) is a large group of animals that includes octopuses, snails, and scallops. Octopuses and their relatives —including squid and cuttlefish—form the class Cephalopoda. Cephalopods typically have a head with a radula (a file-like feeding organ) and beak; a well-developed nervous system; sucker-bearing tentacles; a muscular mantle (part of the body wall) that can expel water through the siphon, enabling movement by jet propulsion; and a small shell or no shell. Snails and their relatives—including slugs, limpets, and abalones—make up the class Gastropoda. Gastropods typically have a coiled external shell, although some, such as slugs, have a small internal shell or no shell; a flat foot; and a head with tentacles and a radula. Scallops and their relatives—including clams, mussels, and oysters—make up the class Bivalvia (also called Pelecypoda). Features of bivalves include a shell with two halves (valves); large gills that are used for breathing and filter feeding; and no radula.

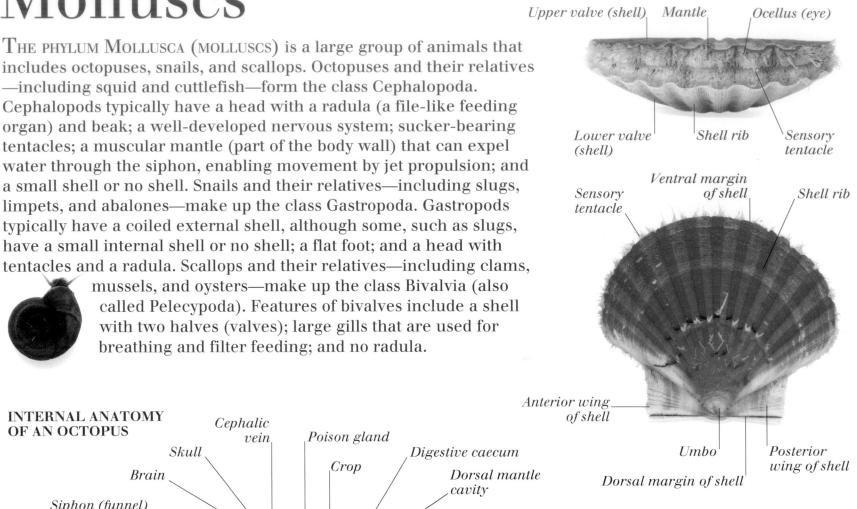

EXTERNAL FEATURES OF A SCALLOP

Upper valve (shell)   Mantle   Ocellus (eye)

Lower valve (shell)   Shell rib   Sensory tentacle

Sensory tentacle   Ventral margin of shell   Shell rib

Anterior wing of shell

Umbo   Posterior wing of shell

Dorsal margin of shell

INTERNAL ANATOMY OF AN OCTOPUS

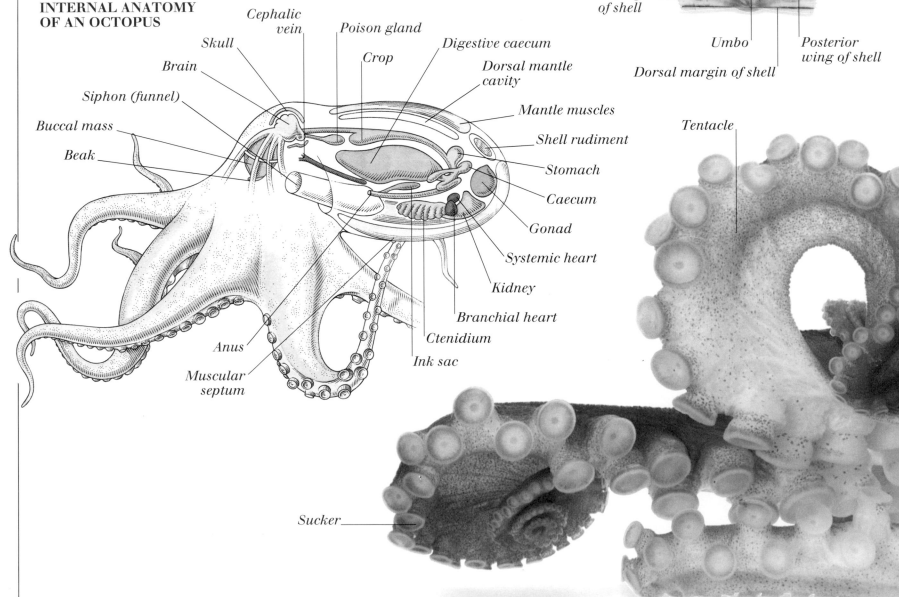

Cephalic vein
Poison gland
Skull
Crop
Digestive caecum
Brain
Dorsal mantle cavity
Siphon (funnel)
Mantle muscles
Buccal mass
Shell rudiment
Beak
Stomach
Caecum
Gonad
Systemic heart
Kidney
Branchial heart
Ctenidium
Anus
Ink sac
Muscular septum

Tentacle

Sucker

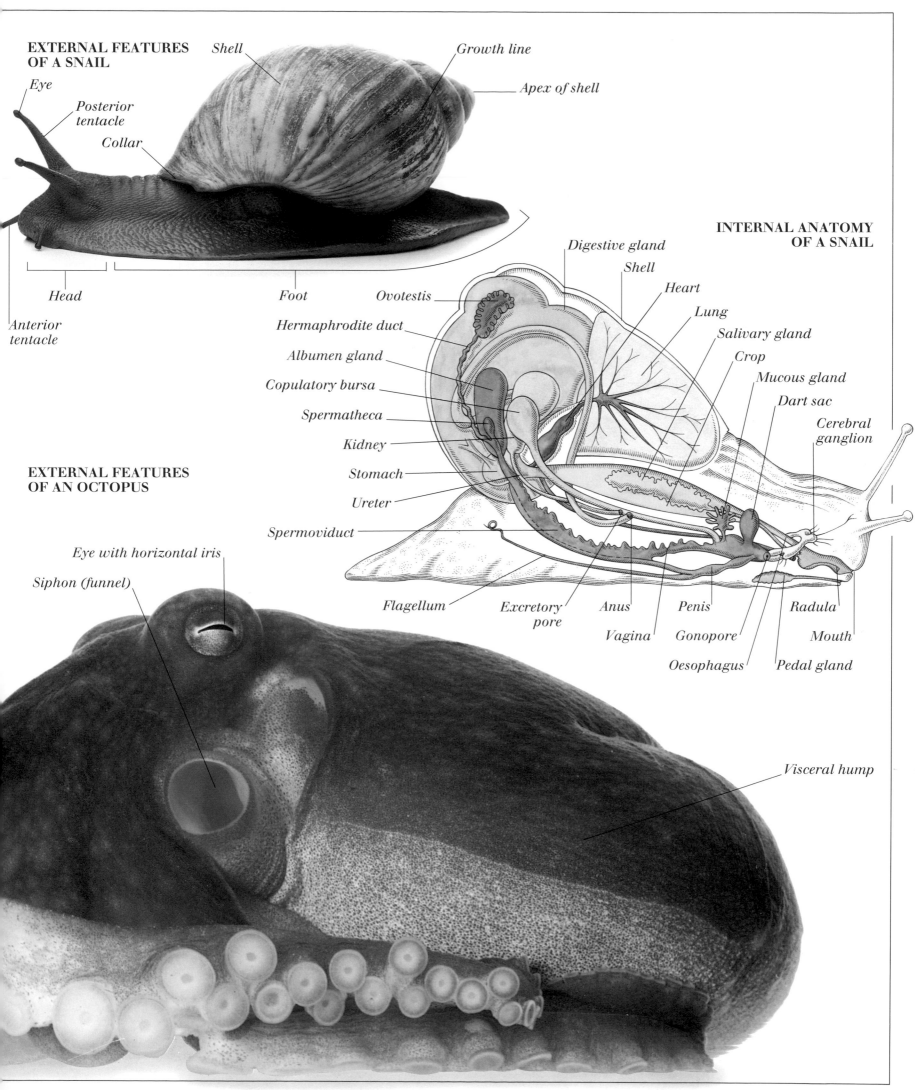

EXTERNAL FEATURES OF A SNAIL

Shell
Growth line
Eye
Apex of shell
Posterior tentacle
Collar
Head
Foot
Anterior tentacle

INTERNAL ANATOMY OF A SNAIL

Digestive gland
Shell
Heart
Ovotestis
Lung
Hermaphrodite duct
Salivary gland
Albumen gland
Crop
Copulatory bursa
Mucous gland
Dart sac
Spermatheca
Cerebral ganglion
Kidney
Stomach
Ureter
Spermoviduct
Flagellum
Excretory pore
Anus
Penis
Radula
Vagina
Gonopore
Mouth
Oesophagus
Pedal gland

EXTERNAL FEATURES OF AN OCTOPUS

Eye with horizontal iris
Siphon (funnel)
Visceral hump

Crustaceans

THE SUBPHYLUM CRUSTACEA is one of the largest groups in the phylum Arthropoda. The subphylum is divided into several classes, the most important of which are Malacostraca and Cirripedia. The class Malacostraca includes crayfish, crabs, lobsters, and shrimps. Typical features of malacostracans include a body divided into two sections (a combined head and thorax called a cephalothorax, and an abdomen); an exoskeleton (external skeleton) with a large plate (carapace) covering the cephalothorax; stalked, compound eyes; and two pairs of antennae. The class Cirripedia includes barnacles, which, unlike other crustaceans, spend their adult lives attached to a surface, such as a rock. Other characteristics of cirripedes include an exoskeleton of overlapping calcareous plates; a body consisting almost entirely of thorax (the abdomen and head are minute); and six pairs of thoracic appendages (cirri) used for filter feeding.

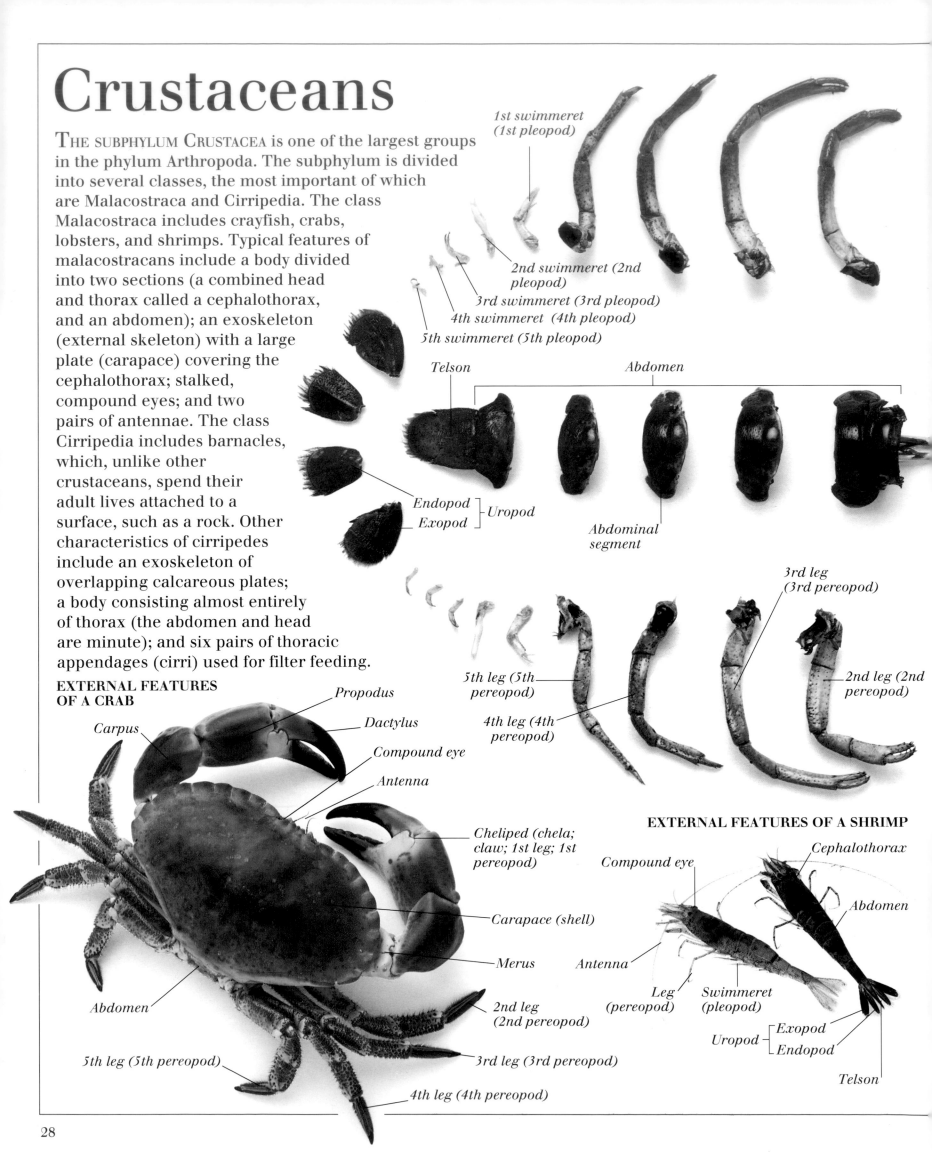

1st swimmeret (1st pleopod)

2nd swimmeret (2nd pleopod)

3rd swimmeret (3rd pleopod)

4th swimmeret (4th pleopod)

5th swimmeret (5th pleopod)

Telson

Abdomen

Endopod · Exopod ⎫ Uropod

Abdominal segment

3rd leg (3rd pereopod)

5th leg (5th pereopod)

4th leg (4th pereopod)

2nd leg (2nd pereopod)

EXTERNAL FEATURES OF A CRAB

Propodus

Dactylus

Carpus

Compound eye

Antenna

Cheliped (chela; claw; 1st leg; 1st pereopod)

Carapace (shell)

Merus

Abdomen

2nd leg (2nd pereopod)

5th leg (5th pereopod)

3rd leg (3rd pereopod)

4th leg (4th pereopod)

EXTERNAL FEATURES OF A SHRIMP

Compound eye

Cephalothorax

Abdomen

Antenna

Leg (pereopod)

Swimmeret (pleopod)

Uropod ⎡ Exopod ⎣ Endopod

Telson

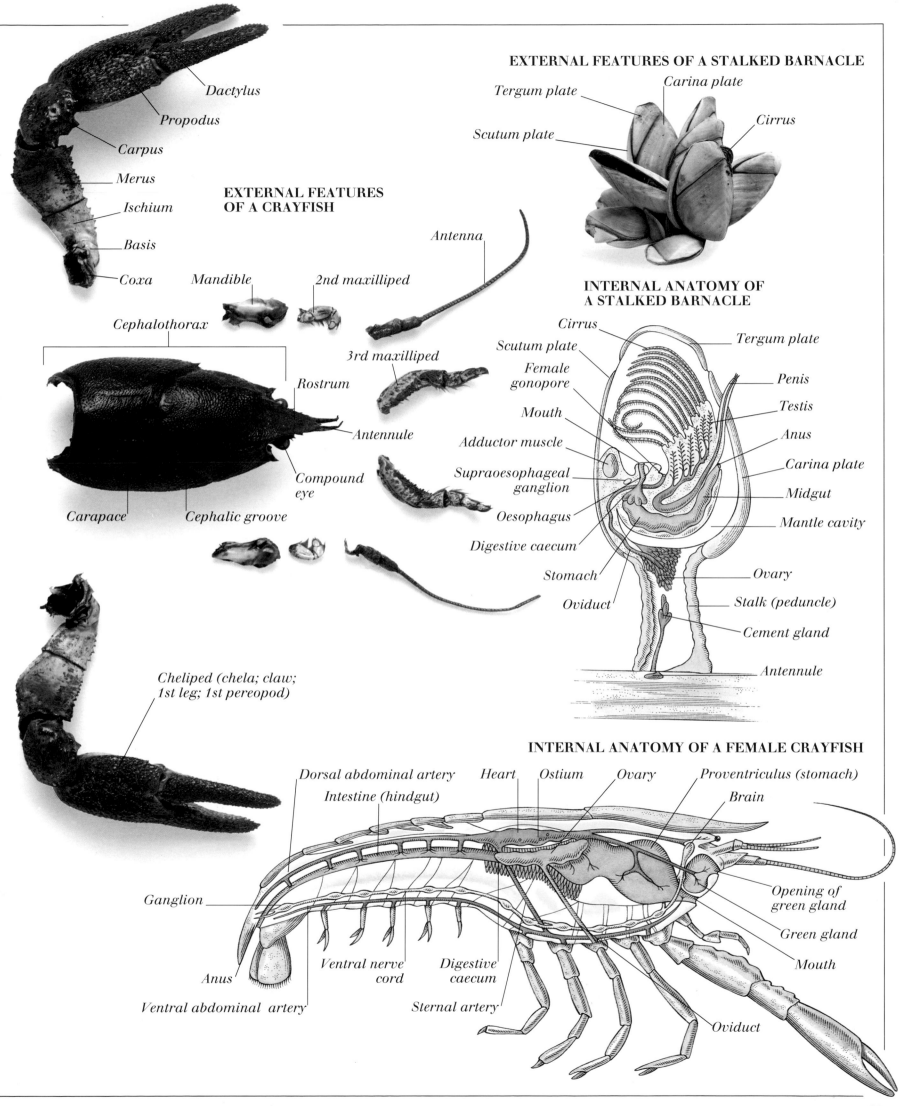

EXTERNAL FEATURES OF A CRAYFISH

Dactylus
Propodus
Carpus
Merus
Ischium
Basis
Coxa

Mandible
2nd maxilliped
Antenna
3rd maxilliped
Cephalothorax
Rostrum
Antennule
Compound eye
Carapace
Cephalic groove

Cheliped (chela; claw; 1st leg; 1st pereopod)

EXTERNAL FEATURES OF A STALKED BARNACLE

Tergum plate
Carina plate
Scutum plate
Cirrus

INTERNAL ANATOMY OF A STALKED BARNACLE

Cirrus
Tergum plate
Scutum plate
Female gonopore
Penis
Testis
Mouth
Adductor muscle
Anus
Supraoesophageal ganglion
Carina plate
Midgut
Oesophagus
Mantle cavity
Digestive caecum
Stomach
Ovary
Oviduct
Stalk (peduncle)
Cement gland
Antennule

INTERNAL ANATOMY OF A FEMALE CRAYFISH

Dorsal abdominal artery
Heart
Ostium
Ovary
Proventriculus (stomach)
Intestine (hindgut)
Brain
Ganglion
Opening of green gland
Green gland
Anus
Mouth
Ventral nerve cord
Digestive caecum
Ventral abdominal artery
Sternal artery
Oviduct

29

Amphibians

THE CLASS AMPHIBIA INCLUDES FROGS and toads (which make up the order Anura), and newts and salamanders (which make up the order Urodela). Amphibians typically have moist, scaleless, hairless skin; lungs; and are cold-blooded. They also undergo complete metamorphosis, from eggs laid in water through various water-living larval stages (such as tadpoles) to land-living adults. Typical features of adult frogs and toads include a squat body with no tail; long, powerful hind legs; and large, often bulging, eyes. Adult newts and salamanders typically have a long body with a well-developed tail; and relatively short, equal-sized legs. However, newts and salamanders show considerable variation; for example, in some species the adults have minute legs, external gills rather than lungs, and spend their entire lives in water.

INTERNAL ANATOMY OF A FEMALE FROG

EXTERNAL FEATURES OF A FROG

Hind limb
Trunk
Head
Forelimb
5 digits
Tympanum (eardrum)
Web
4 digits
External nostril
Mouth
Eye

EXTERNAL FEATURES OF A SALAMANDER

Eye
Tail
Forelimb
Hind limb
Digit

Larynx
Right bronchus
Stomach
Right lung
Heart
Liver
Posterior vena cava
Right kidney
Dorsal aorta
Cloaca
Rectum
Pulmonary artery
Left lung
Pancreas
Duodenum
Spleen
Left kidney
Mesentery
Small intestine (ileum)
Left ureter

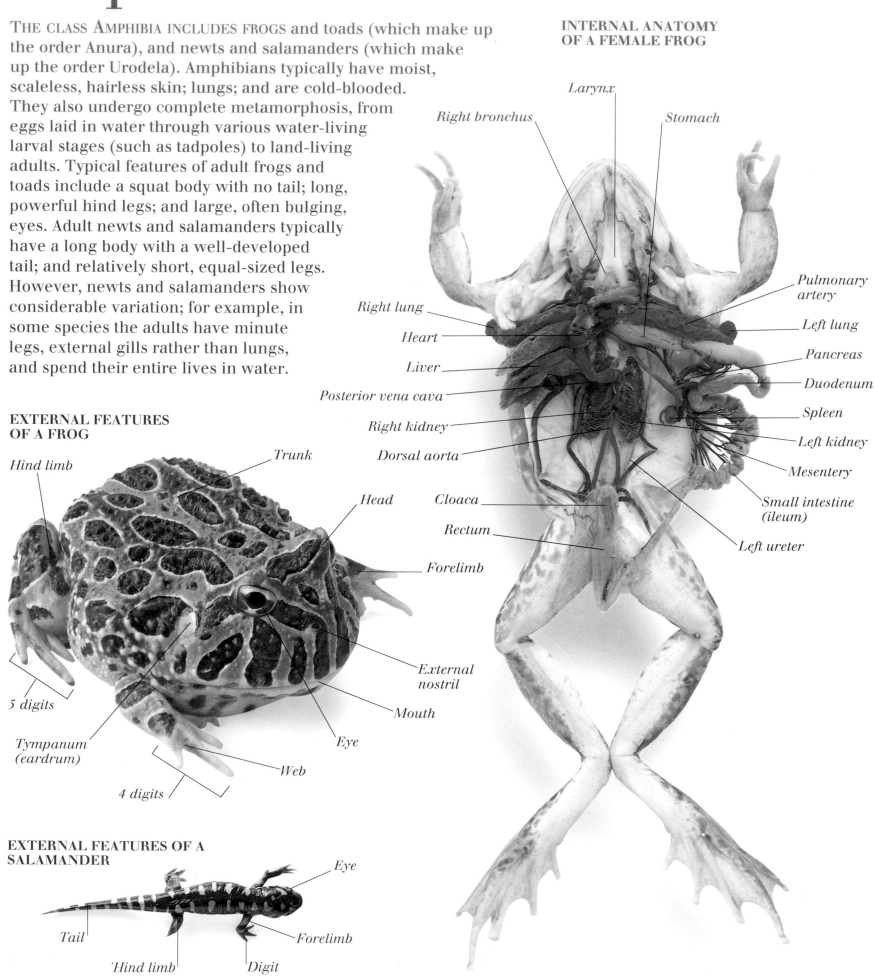

EGGS (SPAWN)

YOUNG TADPOLES

MATURE TADPOLE

YOUNG FROG

METAMORPHOSIS OF FROGS

Frogs undergo complete metamorphosis. Eggs
(spawn) are laid in water and hatch into young
tadpoles, which have a tail and external gills
but no legs. As the tadpoles grow, the gills
disappear, back legs develop, then front
legs, and the tail shrinks. Eventually
the tail disappears, resulting in a
young adult frog.

SKELETON OF A FROG

Premaxilla

*Sphenethmoid
bone*

Nasal bone

Maxilla

Frontoparietal bone

Pterygoid bone

Pro-otic bone

Quadratojugal bone

Phalanges

Squamosal bone

Exoccipital bone

Suprascapula

Metacarpals

Vertebra

Radio-ulna

Carpals

Phalanges

Humerus

Metatarsal

*Sacral
vertebra*

Ilium

*Distal
tarsals*

*Proximal
tarsals*

*Astragalus
(tibiale)*

*Calcaneum
(fibulare)*

Femur

Urostyle

Tibiofibula

Ischium

Lizards and snakes

LIZARDS AND SNAKES BELONG to the order Squamata, a division of the class Reptilia. Characteristic reptilian features include scaly skin, lungs, and cold-bloodedness. Most reptiles lay leathery-shelled eggs, although some hatch the eggs inside their bodies and give birth to live young. Lizards belong to the suborder Lacertilia. Typically, they have long tails, and shed their skin in several pieces. Many lizards can regenerate a tail if it is lost; some can change colour; and some are limbless. Snakes make up the suborder Ophidia (also called Serpentes). All snakes have long, limbless bodies; can dislocate their lower jaw to swallow large prey; and have eyelids that are joined together to form a single transparent covering over the front of the eye. Most snakes shed their skin in a single piece. Constrictor snakes kill their prey by squeezing; venomous snakes poison their prey.

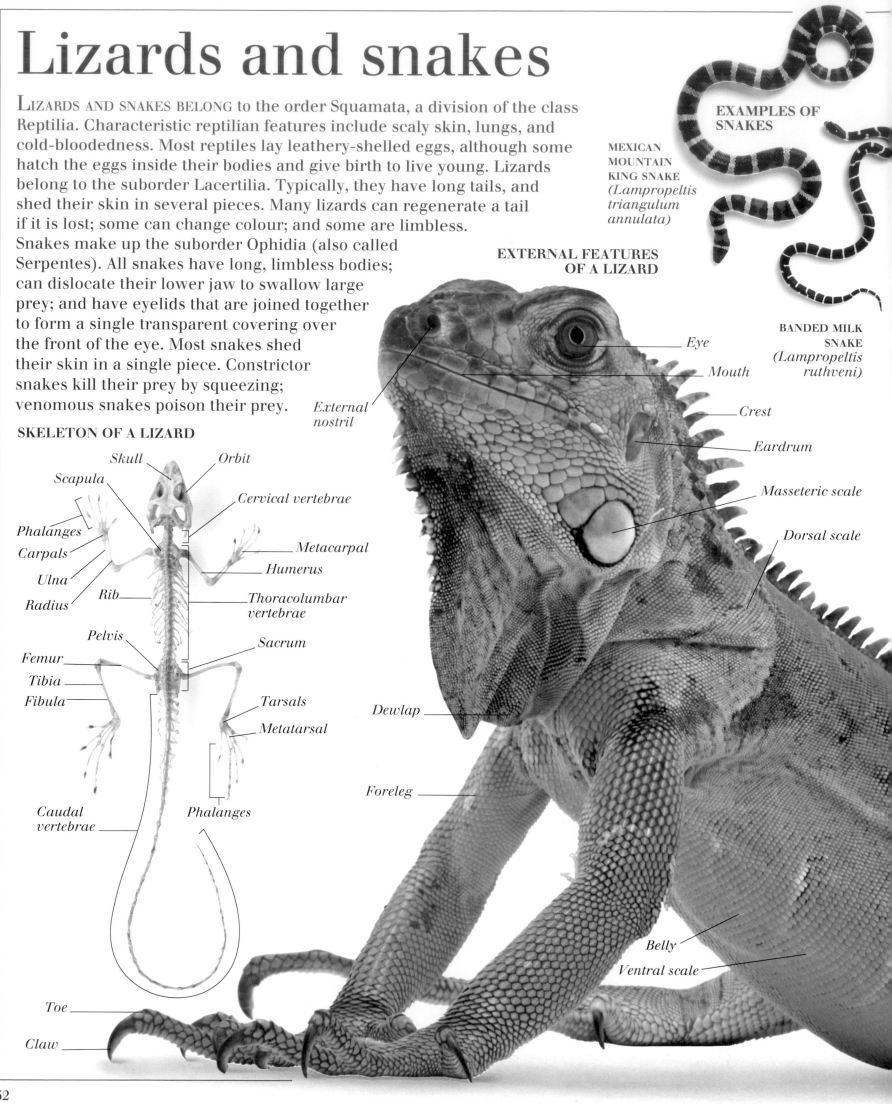

EXAMPLES OF SNAKES

MEXICAN MOUNTAIN KING SNAKE (*Lampropeltis triangulum annulata*)

BANDED MILK SNAKE (*Lampropeltis ruthveni*)

EXTERNAL FEATURES OF A LIZARD

External nostril

Eye

Mouth

Crest

Eardrum

Masseteric scale

Dorsal scale

Dewlap

Foreleg

Belly

Ventral scale

SKELETON OF A LIZARD

Skull

Orbit

Scapula

Cervical vertebrae

Phalanges

Carpals

Metacarpal

Humerus

Ulna

Radius

Rib

Thoracolumbar vertebrae

Pelvis

Sacrum

Femur

Tibia

Fibula

Tarsals

Metatarsal

Caudal vertebrae

Phalanges

Toe

Claw

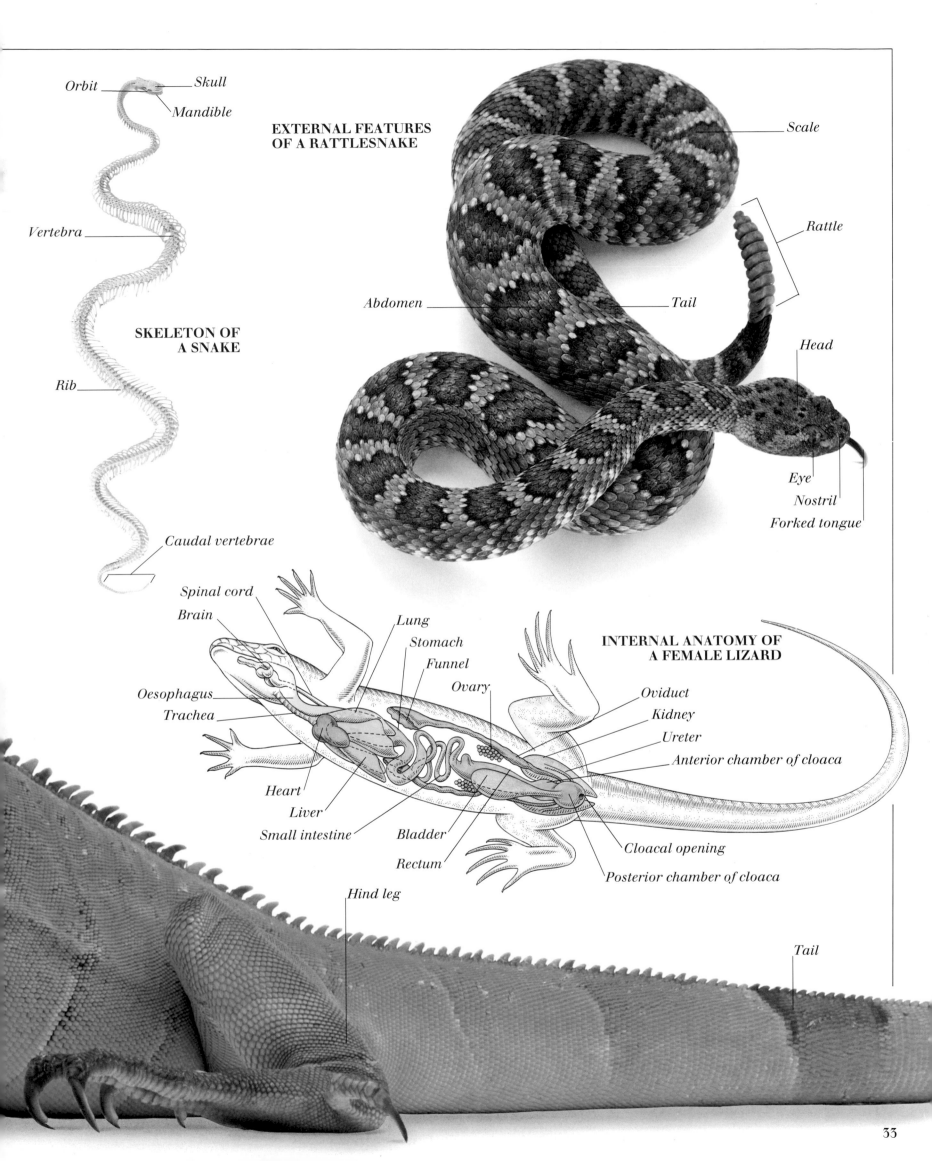

SKELETON OF A SNAKE

Orbit

Skull

Mandible

Vertebra

Rib

Caudal vertebrae

EXTERNAL FEATURES OF A RATTLESNAKE

Scale

Rattle

Abdomen

Tail

Head

Eye

Nostril

Forked tongue

INTERNAL ANATOMY OF A FEMALE LIZARD

Spinal cord

Brain

Lung

Stomach

Funnel

Ovary

Oesophagus

Trachea

Oviduct

Kidney

Ureter

Anterior chamber of cloaca

Heart

Liver

Small intestine

Bladder

Rectum

Cloacal opening

Posterior chamber of cloaca

Hind leg

Tail

33

Crocodilians and turtles

CROCODILIANS AND TURTLES BELONG to different orders in the class Reptilia. The order Crocodilia includes crocodiles, alligators, caimans, and gharials. Typically, crocodilians are carnivores (flesh-eaters), and have a long snout, sharp teeth for gripping prey, and hard, square scales. All crocodilians are adapted to living on land and in water: they have four strong legs for moving on land; a powerful tail for swimming; and their eyes and nostrils are high on the head so that they stay above water while the rest of the body is submerged. The order Chelonia includes marine turtles, terrapins (freshwater turtles), and tortoises (land turtles). Characteristically, chelonians have a short, broad body encased in a bony shell with an outer horny covering, into which the head and limbs can be withdrawn; and a horny beak instead of teeth.

GHARIAL
(Gavialis gangeticus)

NILE CROCODILE
(Crocodylus niloticus)

AMERICAN ALLIGATOR
(Alligator mississippiensis)

SKELETON OF A CROCODILE

Skull · Mandible · Cervical vertebrae · Thoracic vertebrae · Lumbar vertebrae · Sacrum · Caudal vertebrae · Scapula · Humerus · Radius · Ulna · Rib · Femur · Fibula · Phalanges · Metatarsals · Tarsals · Tibia

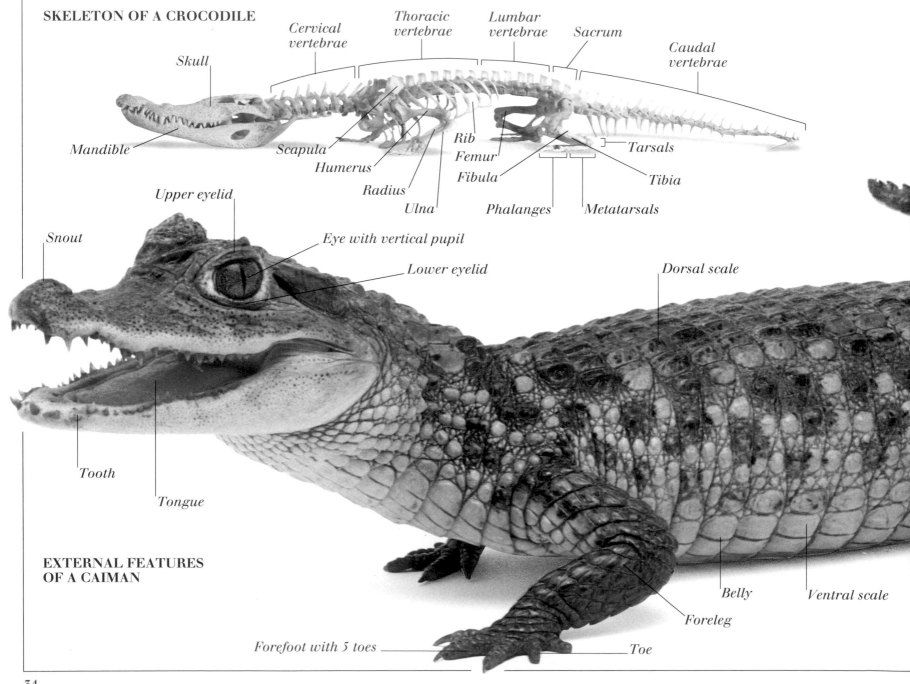

Upper eyelid · Eye with vertical pupil · Lower eyelid · Snout · Tooth · Tongue · Dorsal scale · Belly · Ventral scale · Foreleg · Forefoot with 5 toes · Toe

EXTERNAL FEATURES OF A CAIMAN

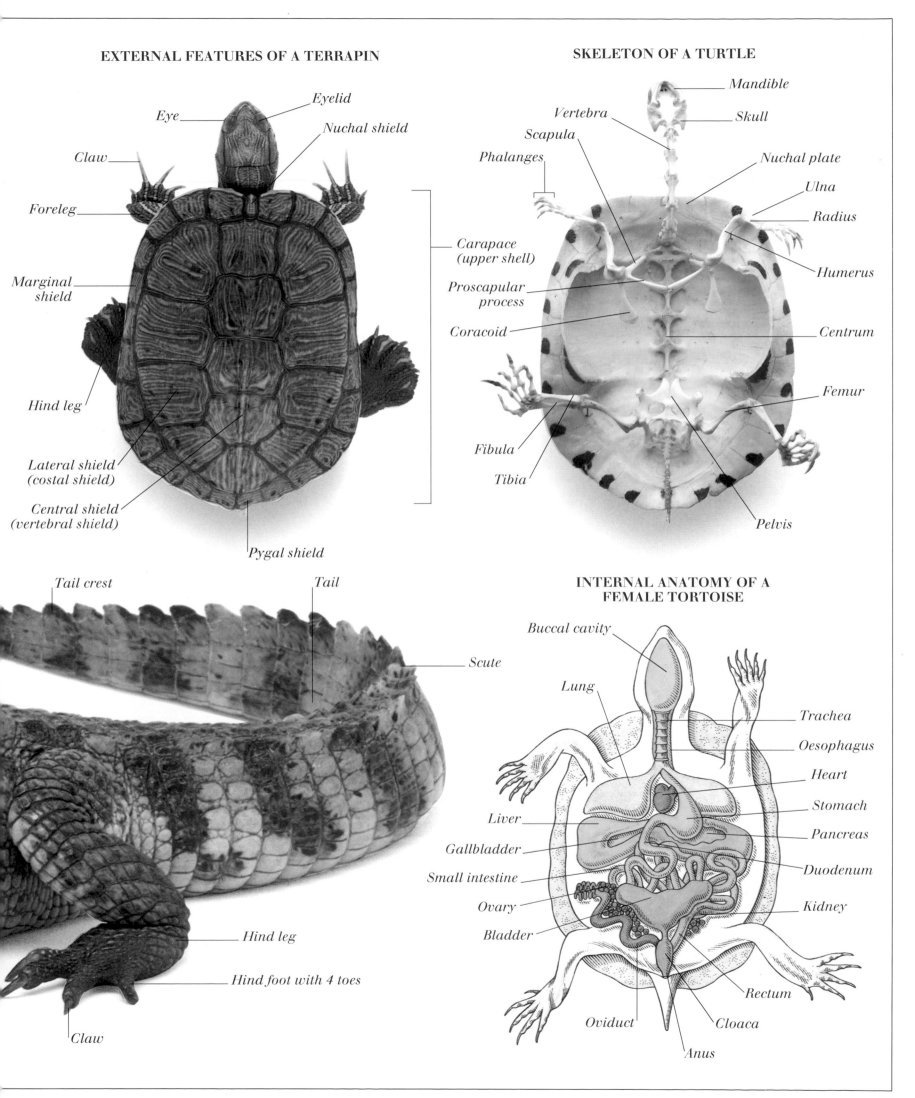

EXTERNAL FEATURES OF A TERRAPIN

Eye

Eyelid

Nuchal shield

Claw

Foreleg

Marginal shield

Hind leg

Lateral shield (costal shield)

Central shield (vertebral shield)

Pygal shield

Carapace (upper shell)

SKELETON OF A TURTLE

Mandible

Vertebra

Skull

Scapula

Phalanges

Nuchal plate

Ulna

Radius

Humerus

Proscapular process

Coracoid

Centrum

Femur

Fibula

Tibia

Pelvis

Tail crest

Tail

Scute

Hind leg

Hind foot with 4 toes

Claw

INTERNAL ANATOMY OF A FEMALE TORTOISE

Buccal cavity

Lung

Trachea

Oesophagus

Heart

Stomach

Liver

Pancreas

Gallbladder

Duodenum

Small intestine

Ovary

Kidney

Bladder

Oviduct

Rectum

Cloaca

Anus

Birds 1

BIRDS MAKE UP THE CLASS AVES. There are more than 9,000 species, almost all of which can fly (the only flightless birds are penguins, ostriches, rheas, cassowaries, and kiwis). The ability to fly is reflected in the typical bird features: forelimbs modified as wings; a streamlined body; and hollow bones to reduce weight. All birds lay hard-shelled eggs, which the parents incubate. Birds' beaks and feet vary according to diet and way of life. Beaks range from general-purpose types suitable for a mixed diet (those of thrushes, for example), to types specialized for particular foods (such as the large, curved, sieving beaks of flamingos). Feet range from the webbed "paddles" of ducks, to the talons of birds of prey. Plumage also varies widely, and in many species the male is brightly coloured for courtship display whereas the female is drab.

EXTERNAL FEATURES OF A BIRD

Forehead

Eye

Crown

Nostril

Nape

Upper mandible

Beak

Lower mandible

Chin

Throat

EXAMPLES OF BIRDS

MALE TUFTED DUCK
(*Aythya fuligula*)

WHITE STORK
(*Ciconia ciconia*)

MALE OSTRICH
(*Struthio camelus*)

Minor coverts

Lesser wing coverts

Median wing coverts

Greater wing coverts
(major coverts)

Secondary flight feathers
(secondary remiges)

Primary flight feathers
(primary remiges)

Breast

Belly

Flank

Thigh

Under tail coverts

Tarsus

Claw

Toe

Tail feathers (retrices)

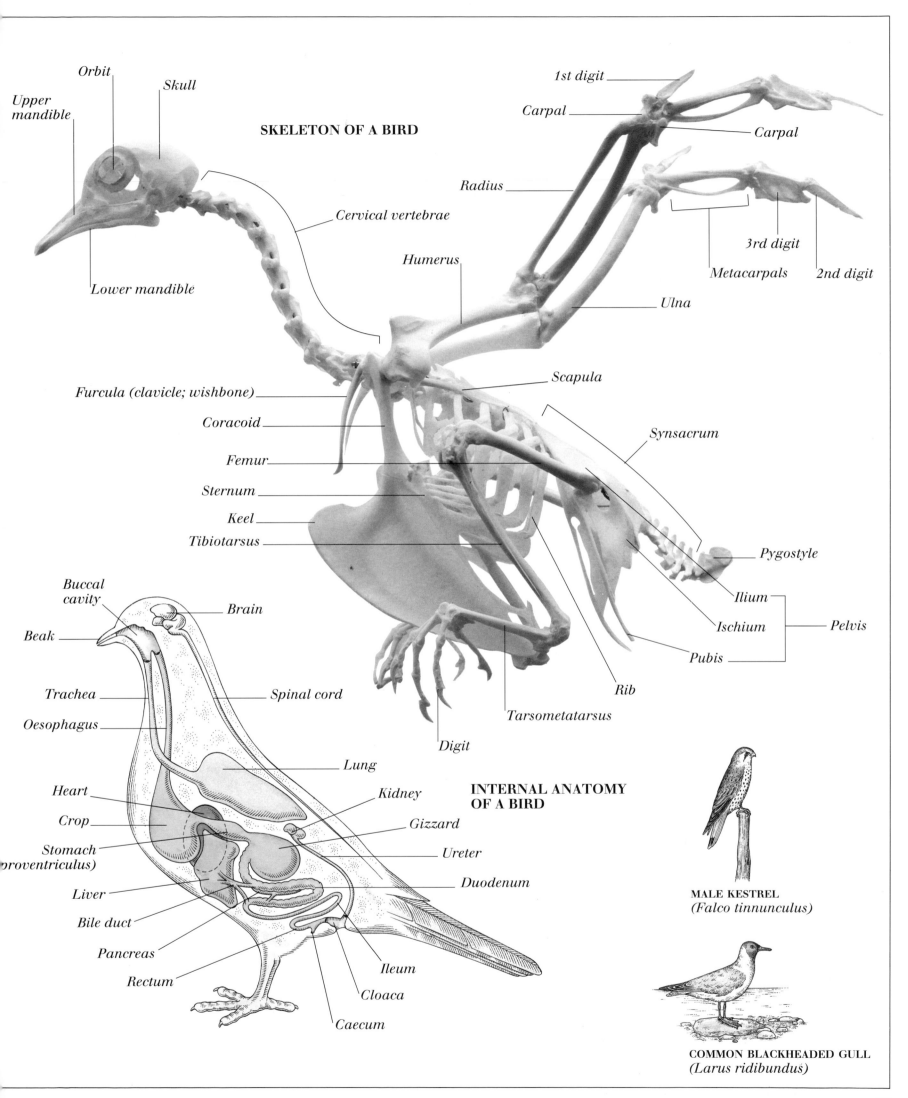

SKELETON OF A BIRD

Upper mandible

Orbit

Skull

1st digit

Carpal

Carpal

Radius

Cervical vertebrae

3rd digit

Metacarpals

2nd digit

Humerus

Ulna

Lower mandible

Scapula

Furcula (clavicle; wishbone)

Synsacrum

Coracoid

Femur

Sternum

Keel

Tibiotarsus

Pygostyle

Ilium

Ischium

Pelvis

Pubis

Rib

Buccal cavity

Brain

Tarsometatarsus

Beak

Spinal cord

Digit

Trachea

Oesophagus

Lung

Kidney

INTERNAL ANATOMY OF A BIRD

Heart

Gizzard

Crop

Ureter

Stomach (proventriculus)

Duodenum

Liver

Bile duct

Pancreas

Ileum

Rectum

Cloaca

Caecum

MALE KESTREL
(Falco tinnunculus)

COMMON BLACKHEADED GULL
(Larus ridibundus)

Birds 2

EXAMPLES OF BIRDS' FEET

KITTIWAKE
(Rissa tridactyla)
The webbed feet are
adapted for paddling
through water.

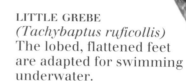

LITTLE GREBE
(Tachybaptus ruficollis)
The lobed, flattened feet
are adapted for swimming
underwater.

TAWNY OWL
(Strix aluco)
The clawed feet are adapted
for gripping prey.

EXAMPLES OF BIRDS' BEAKS

KING VULTURE
(Sarcorhamphus papa)
The hooked beak is adapted
for pulling apart flesh.

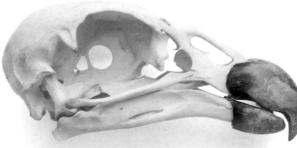

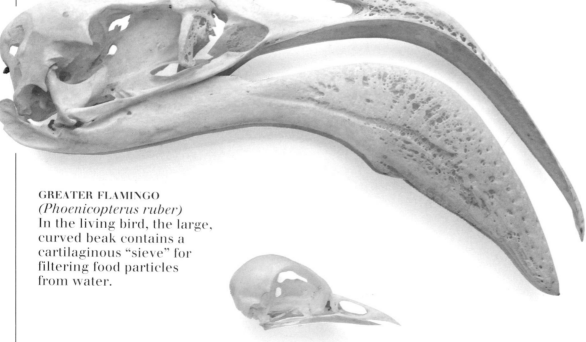

GREATER FLAMINGO
(Phoenicopterus ruber)
In the living bird, the large,
curved beak contains a
cartilaginous "sieve" for
filtering food particles
from water.

MISTLE THRUSH
(Turdus viscivorus)
The general-purpose beak is
suitable for a wide range of animal
and plant foods.

BLUE-AND-YELLOW MACAW
(Ara ararauna)
The broad, powerful, hooked beak
is adapted for crushing seeds and
eating fruit.

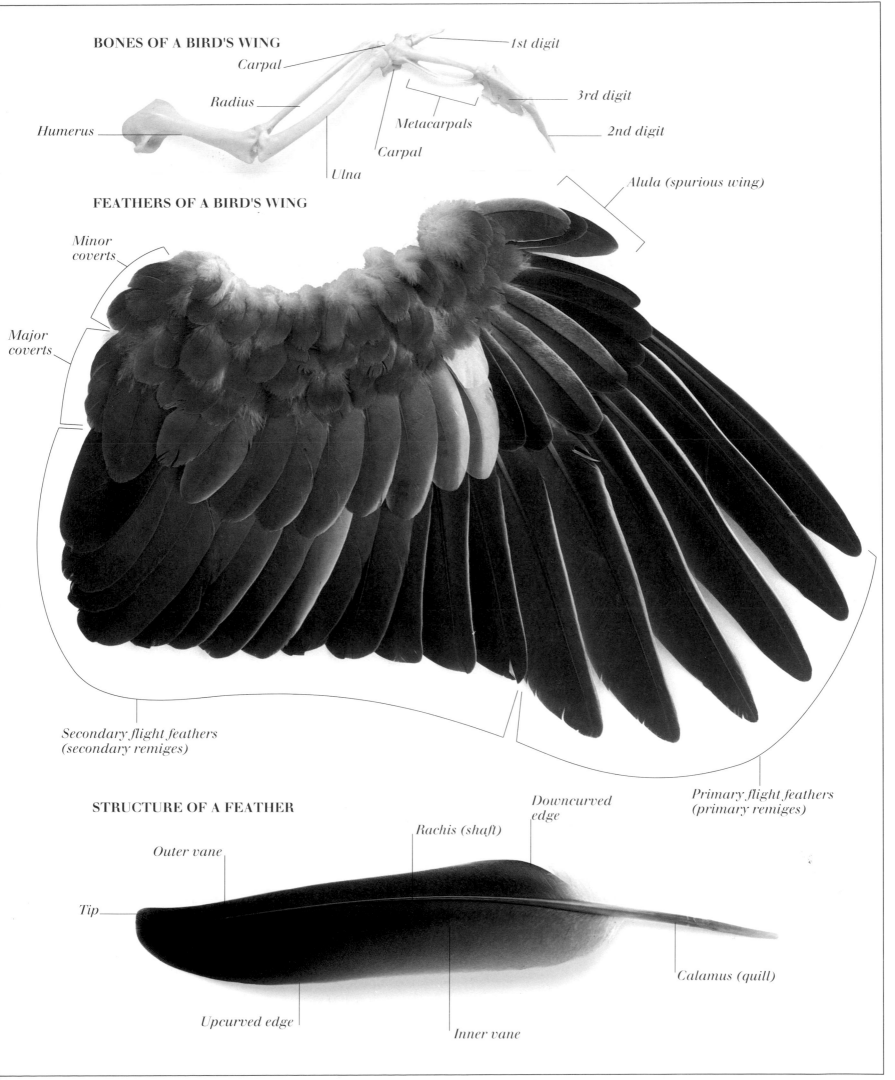

BONES OF A BIRD'S WING

Carpal
1st digit
Radius
3rd digit
Humerus
Metacarpals
2nd digit
Carpal
Ulna
Alula (spurious wing)

FEATHERS OF A BIRD'S WING

Minor coverts
Major coverts
Secondary flight feathers (secondary remiges)
Primary flight feathers (primary remiges)

STRUCTURE OF A FEATHER

Downcurved edge
Rachis (shaft)
Outer vane
Tip
Calamus (quill)
Upcurved edge
Inner vane

Eggs

AN EGG IS A SINGLE CELL, produced by the female, with the capacity to develop into a new individual. Development may take place inside the mother's body (as in most mammals) or outside, in which case the egg has a protective covering such as a shell. Egg yolk nourishes the growing young. Eggs developing inside the mother generally have little yolk, because the young are nourished from her body. Eggs developing outside may also have little yolk if they are produced by animals whose young go through a larval stage (such as a caterpillar) that feeds itself while developing into the adult form. The shelled eggs of birds and reptiles contain enough yolk to sustain the young until it hatches into a juvenile version of the adult.

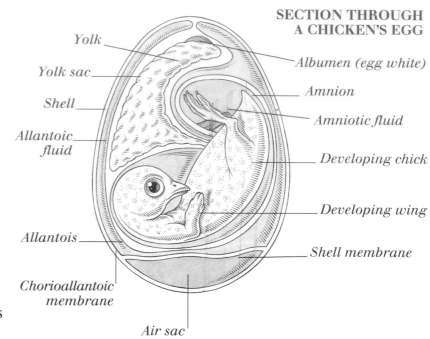

SECTION THROUGH A CHICKEN'S EGG

Yolk
Yolk sac
Shell
Allantoic fluid
Allantois
Chorioallantoic membrane
Air sac
Albumen (egg white)
Amnion
Amniotic fluid
Developing chick
Developing wing
Shell membrane

VARIETY OF EGGS

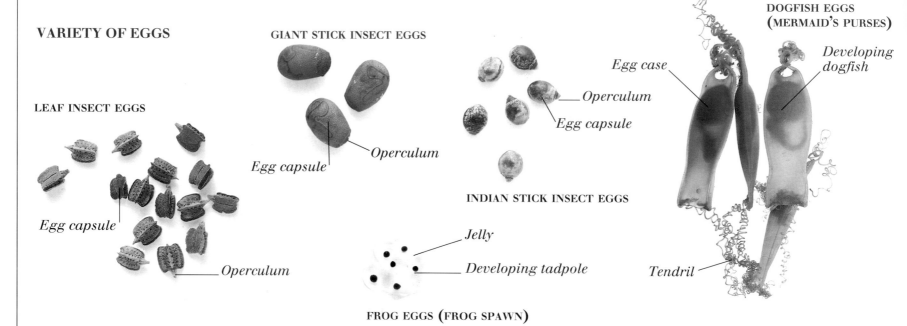

LEAF INSECT EGGS

Egg capsule
Operculum

GIANT STICK INSECT EGGS

Egg capsule
Operculum

INDIAN STICK INSECT EGGS

Operculum
Egg capsule

FROG EGGS (FROG SPAWN)

Jelly
Developing tadpole

DOGFISH EGGS (MERMAID'S PURSES)

Egg case
Developing dogfish
Tendril

HATCHING OF A QUAIL'S EGG

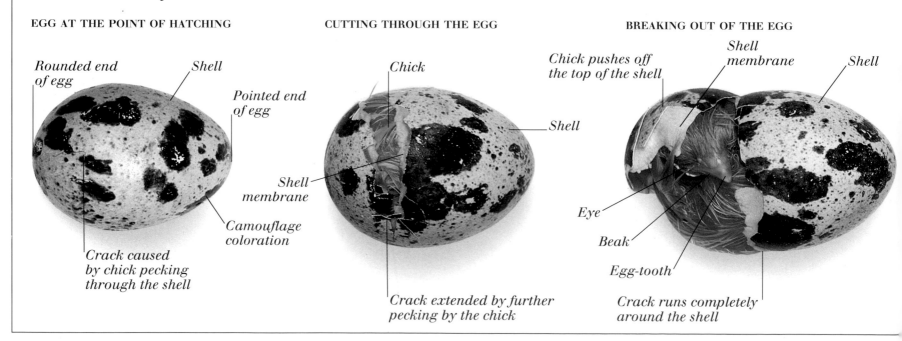

EGG AT THE POINT OF HATCHING

Rounded end of egg
Shell
Pointed end of egg
Shell membrane
Camouflage coloration
Crack caused by chick pecking through the shell

CUTTING THROUGH THE EGG

Chick
Shell
Shell membrane
Crack extended by further pecking by the chick

BREAKING OUT OF THE EGG

Chick pushes off the top of the shell
Shell membrane
Shell
Eye
Beak
Egg-tooth
Crack runs completely around the shell

EXAMPLES OF BIRDS' EGGS

BEE HUMMINGBIRD
(Calypte helenae)

GREATER BLACKBACKED GULL
(Larus marinus)

BALTIMORE ORIOLE
(Icterus galbula)

WILLOW GROUSE
(Lagopus lagopus)

COMMON TERN
(Sterna hirundo)

CARRION CROW
(Corvus corone)

CHAFFINCH
(Fringilla coelebs)

OSTRICH
(Struthio camelus)

EMERGING FROM THE EGG

Eye

Beak

Egg-tooth

Chick heaves itself out of the egg

Tympanum (eardrum)

Shell

Wet down

Remains of egg membranes (amnion and allantois)

THE NEWLY HATCHED CHICK

Eye

Beak

Egg-tooth

Nostril

Tympanum (eardrum)

Chick is dry about an hour after hatching

Dry down

Toe

Claw

Leg

Eggshell

Carnivores

THE MAMMALIAN ORDER CARNIVORA includes cats, dogs, bears, raccoons, pandas, weasels, badgers, skunks, otters, civets, mongooses, and hyenas. The order's name is derived from the fact that most of its members are carnivores (flesh-eaters). Typical carnivore features therefore reflect a hunting life-style: speed and agility; sharp claws and well-developed canine teeth for holding and killing prey; carnassial teeth (cheek teeth) for cutting flesh; and forward-facing eyes for good distance judgment. However, some members of the order—bears, badgers, and foxes, for example—have a more mixed diet, and a few are entirely herbivorous (plant-eating), notably pandas. Such animals have no carnassial teeth and tend to be slower-moving than pure flesh-eaters.

EXTERNAL FEATURES OF A MALE LION

Nose
Eye
Mane
Nostril
Vibrissa (whisker)
Tongue
Canine tooth
Incisor tooth
Chest
Elbow
Lower arm
Toe

SKULL OF A LION

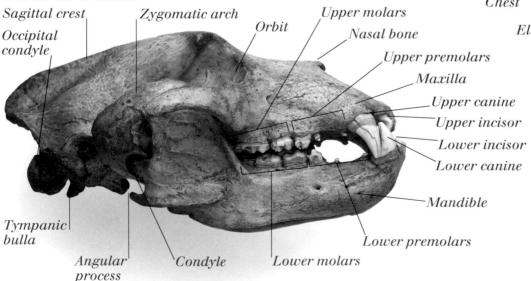

Zygomatic arch
Coronoid process
Sagittal crest
Orbit
Nasal bone
Maxilla
Upper premolars
Upper canine
Lower canine
Mandible
Lower premolars
Occipital condyle
Tympanic bulla
Condyle
Angular process
Upper carnassial tooth (4th upper premolar)

SKULL OF A BEAR

Sagittal crest
Occipital condyle
Zygomatic arch
Orbit
Upper molars
Nasal bone
Upper premolars
Maxilla
Upper canine
Upper incisor
Lower incisor
Lower canine
Mandible
Lower premolars
Tympanic bulla
Angular process
Condyle
Lower molars

EXAMPLES OF CARNIVORES

ALSATIAN DOG
(Canis familiaris)

MANED WOLF
(Chrysocyon brachyurus)

RACCOON
(Procyon lotor)

AMERICAN BLACK BEAR
(Ursus americanus)

SKELETON OF A DOMESTIC CAT

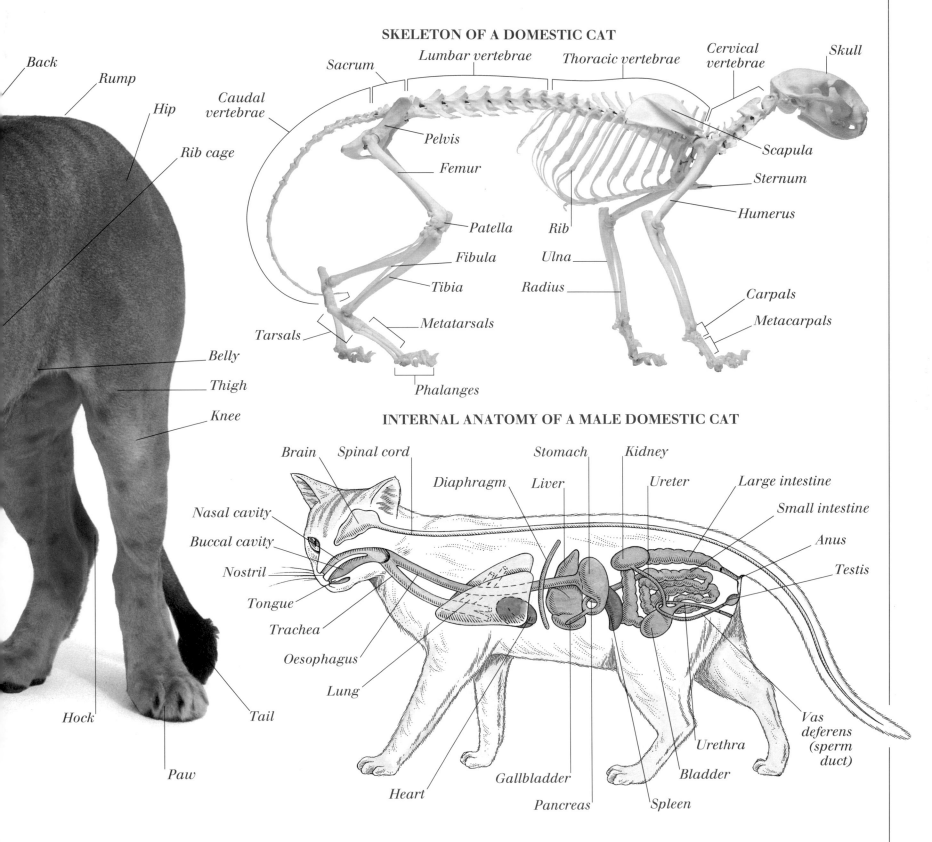

Back

Rump

Hip

Rib cage

Sacrum

Lumbar vertebrae

Thoracic vertebrae

Cervical vertebrae

Skull

Caudal vertebrae

Pelvis

Scapula

Femur

Sternum

Patella

Rib

Humerus

Fibula

Ulna

Tibia

Radius

Carpals

Metatarsals

Metacarpals

Tarsals

Belly

Thigh

Phalanges

Knee

INTERNAL ANATOMY OF A MALE DOMESTIC CAT

Brain

Spinal cord

Stomach

Kidney

Diaphragm

Liver

Ureter

Large intestine

Small intestine

Nasal cavity

Anus

Buccal cavity

Testis

Nostril

Tongue

Trachea

Oesophagus

Hock

Lung

Tail

Vas deferens (sperm duct)

Paw

Heart

Gallbladder

Pancreas

Bladder

Spleen

Urethra

Rabbits and rodents

ALTHOUGH RABBITS AND RODENTS belong to
different orders of mammals, they have some
features in common. These features include
chisel-shaped incisor teeth that grow
continually, and eating their faeces to
extract more nutrients from their plant diet. Rabbits and
hares belong to the order Lagomorpha. Characteristically,
they have four incisors in the upper jaw and two in the
lower jaw; powerful hind legs for jumping; forelimbs
adapted for burrowing; long ears; and a small tail. Rodents
make up the order Rodentia. This is the largest order of
mammals, with more than 1,700 species, including
squirrels, beavers, chipmunks, gophers, rats,
mice, lemmings, gerbils, porcupines, cavies,
and the capybara. Typical rodent features
include two incisors in each jaw;
short forelimbs for manipulating
food; and cheek pouches
for storing food.

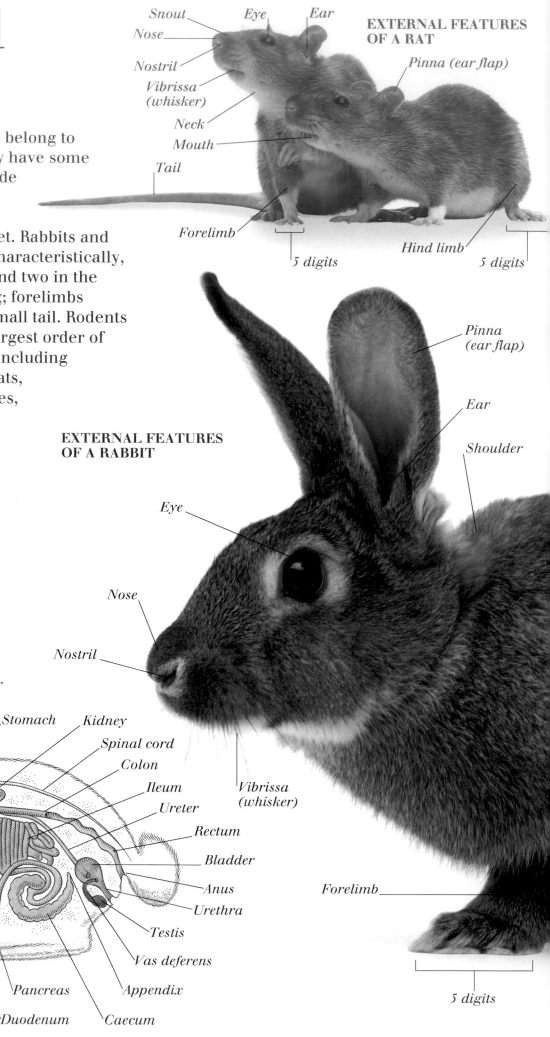

**EXTERNAL FEATURES
OF A RAT**

Snout
Eye
Ear
Nose
Pinna (ear flap)
Nostril
Vibrissa
(whisker)
Neck
Mouth
Tail
Forelimb
5 digits
Hind limb
5 digits

**EXTERNAL FEATURES
OF A RABBIT**

Pinna
(ear flap)
Ear
Shoulder
Eye
Nose
Nostril
Vibrissa
(whisker)
Forelimb
5 digits

**INTERNAL ANATOMY OF
A MALE RABBIT**

Brain
Gallbladder
Liver
Stomach
Kidney
Spinal cord
Colon
Ileum
Ureter
Rectum
Bladder
Anus
Urethra
Testis
Vas deferens
Appendix
Caecum
Duodenum
Pancreas
Diaphragm
Heart
Trachea
Lung
Oesophagus
Tongue
Buccal
cavity
Mouth
Nasal
cavity

44

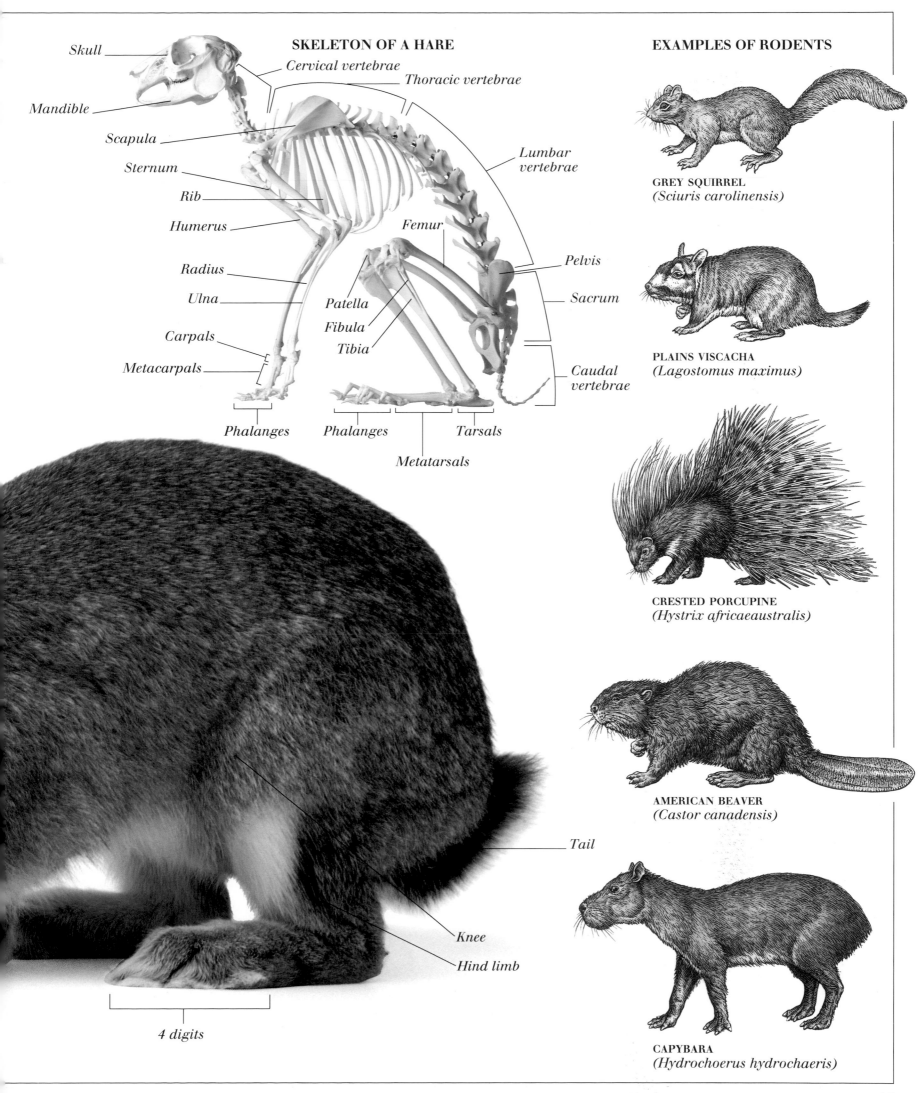

SKELETON OF A HARE

Skull

Mandible

Cervical vertebrae

Thoracic vertebrae

Scapula

Lumbar vertebrae

Sternum

Rib

Humerus

Femur

Radius

Pelvis

Ulna

Patella

Sacrum

Carpals

Fibula

Metacarpals

Tibia

Caudal vertebrae

Phalanges

Phalanges

Tarsals

Metatarsals

Tail

Knee

Hind limb

4 digits

EXAMPLES OF RODENTS

GREY SQUIRREL
(Sciuris carolinensis)

PLAINS VISCACHA
(Lagostomus maximus)

CRESTED PORCUPINE
(Hystrix africaeaustralis)

AMERICAN BEAVER
(Castor canadensis)

CAPYBARA
(Hydrochoerus hydrochaeris)

Ungulates

UNGULATES IS A GENERAL TERM FOR a large, varied group of mammals that includes horses, cattle, and their relatives. The ungulates are divided into two orders on the basis of the number of toes. Members of the order Perissodactyla (odd-toed ungulates) have one or three toes. Perissodactyls include horses, asses, and zebras (all of which are one-toed), and rhinoceroses and tapirs (which are three-toed). Members of the order Artiodactyla (even-toed ungulates) have two or four toes. Most artiodactyls have two toes, which are typically encased in hooves to give the so-called cloven hoof. Two-toed, cloven-hoofed artiodactyls include cows and other cattle, sheep, goats, antelopes, deer, and giraffes. The other main two-toed artiodactyls are camels and llamas. Most two-toed artiodactyls are ruminants; that is, they have a four-chambered stomach and chew the cud. The principal four-toed artiodactyls are pigs, peccaries, and hippopotamuses.

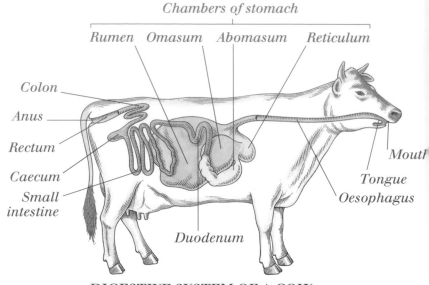

DIGESTIVE SYSTEM OF A COW

**COMPARISON OF THE FRONT FEET
OF A HORSE AND A COW**

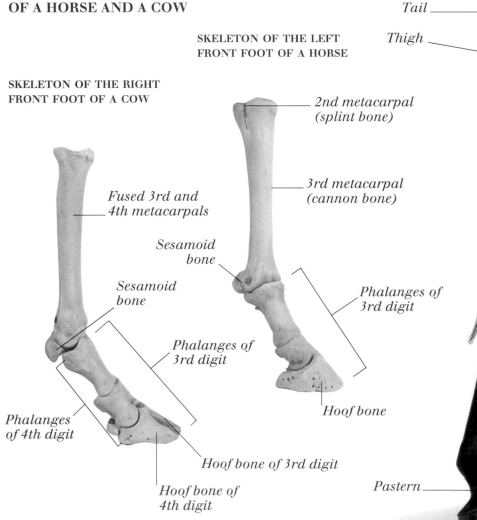

SKELETON OF THE LEFT
FRONT FOOT OF A HORSE

SKELETON OF THE RIGHT
FRONT FOOT OF A COW

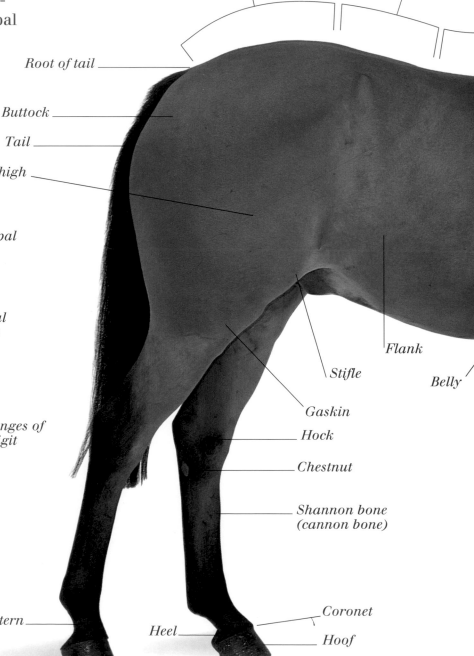

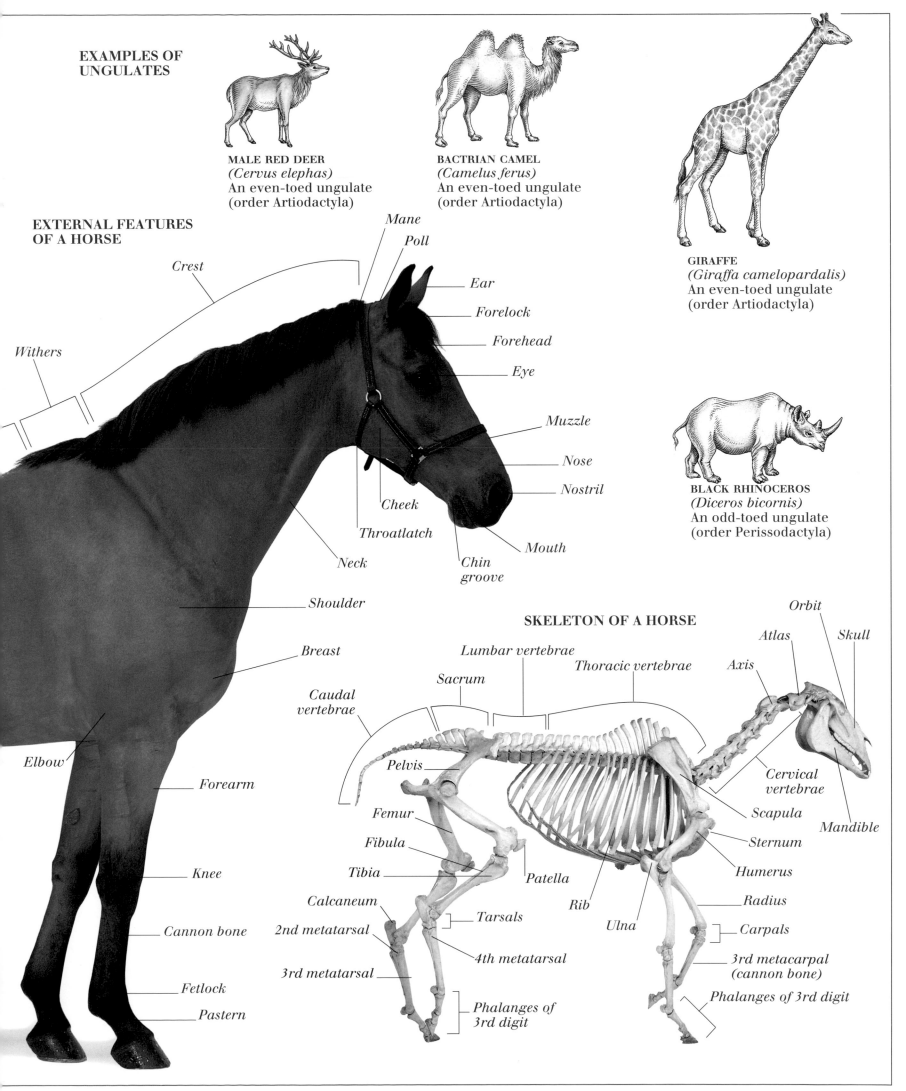

EXAMPLES OF UNGULATES

MALE RED DEER
(Cervus elephas)
An even-toed ungulate
(order Artiodactyla)

BACTRIAN CAMEL
(Camelus ferus)
An even-toed ungulate
(order Artiodactyla)

GIRAFFE
(Giraffa camelopardalis)
An even-toed ungulate
(order Artiodactyla)

BLACK RHINOCEROS
(Diceros bicornis)
An odd-toed ungulate
(order Perissodactyla)

EXTERNAL FEATURES OF A HORSE

Crest

Withers

Mane

Poll

Ear

Forelock

Forehead

Eye

Muzzle

Nose

Nostril

Cheek

Throatlatch

Chin groove

Mouth

Neck

Shoulder

Breast

Elbow

Forearm

Knee

Cannon bone

Fetlock

Pastern

SKELETON OF A HORSE

Caudal vertebrae

Sacrum

Lumbar vertebrae

Thoracic vertebrae

Orbit

Atlas

Skull

Axis

Cervical vertebrae

Pelvis

Scapula

Mandible

Femur

Sternum

Fibula

Humerus

Tibia

Patella

Rib

Radius

Calcaneum

Tarsals

Ulna

Carpals

2nd metatarsal

4th metatarsal

3rd metacarpal
(cannon bone)

3rd metatarsal

Phalanges of
3rd digit

Phalanges of
3rd digit

Elephants

THE TWO SPECIES of elephants—African and Asian—are the only members of the mammalian order Proboscidea. The bigger African elephant is the largest land animal: a fully grown male may be up to 4 m (13 ft) tall and weigh as much as 7 tonnes (6.9 tons). A fully grown male Asian elephant may be 3.3 m (11 ft) tall and weigh 5.4 tonnes (5.3 tons). The trunk—an extension of the nose and upper lip—is the elephant's other most obvious feature. It is used for manipulating and lifting, feeding, drinking and spraying water, smelling, touching, and producing trumpeting sounds. Other characteristic features include a pair of tusks, used for defence and for crushing vegetation; thick, pillar-like legs and broad feet to support the massive body; and large ear flaps that act as radiators to keep the elephant cool.

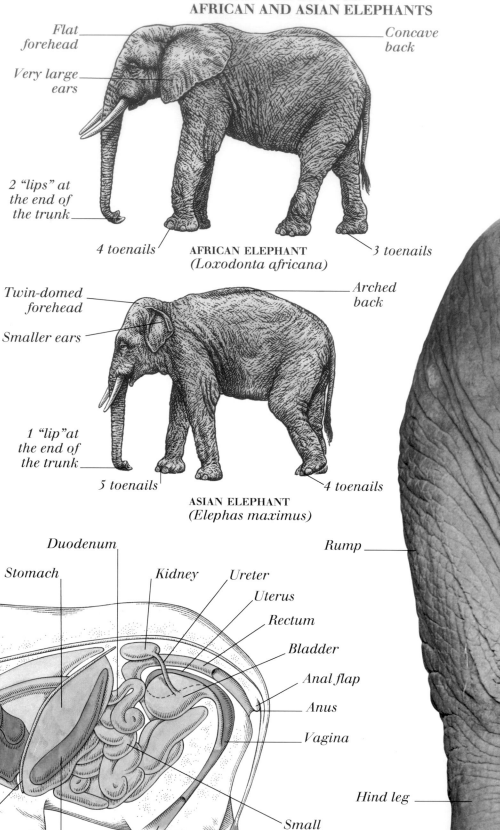

DIFFERENCES BETWEEN AFRICAN AND ASIAN ELEPHANTS

Flat forehead

Concave back

Very large ears

2 "lips" at the end of the trunk

4 toenails

AFRICAN ELEPHANT
(*Loxodonta africana*)

3 toenails

Twin-domed forehead

Arched back

Smaller ears

1 "lip" at the end of the trunk

5 toenails

4 toenails

ASIAN ELEPHANT
(*Elephas maximus*)

Rump

Hind leg

Toenail

INTERNAL ANATOMY OF A FEMALE ELEPHANT

Spinal cord

Heart

Stomach

Duodenum

Kidney

Ureter

Uterus

Rectum

Bladder

Anal flap

Anus

Vagina

Brain

Nasal cavity

Buccal cavity

Mouth

Tongue

Tusk

Epiglottis

Oesophagus

Trachea

Lung

Diaphragm

Nasal passage

Nostril

Spleen

Vulva

Small intestine

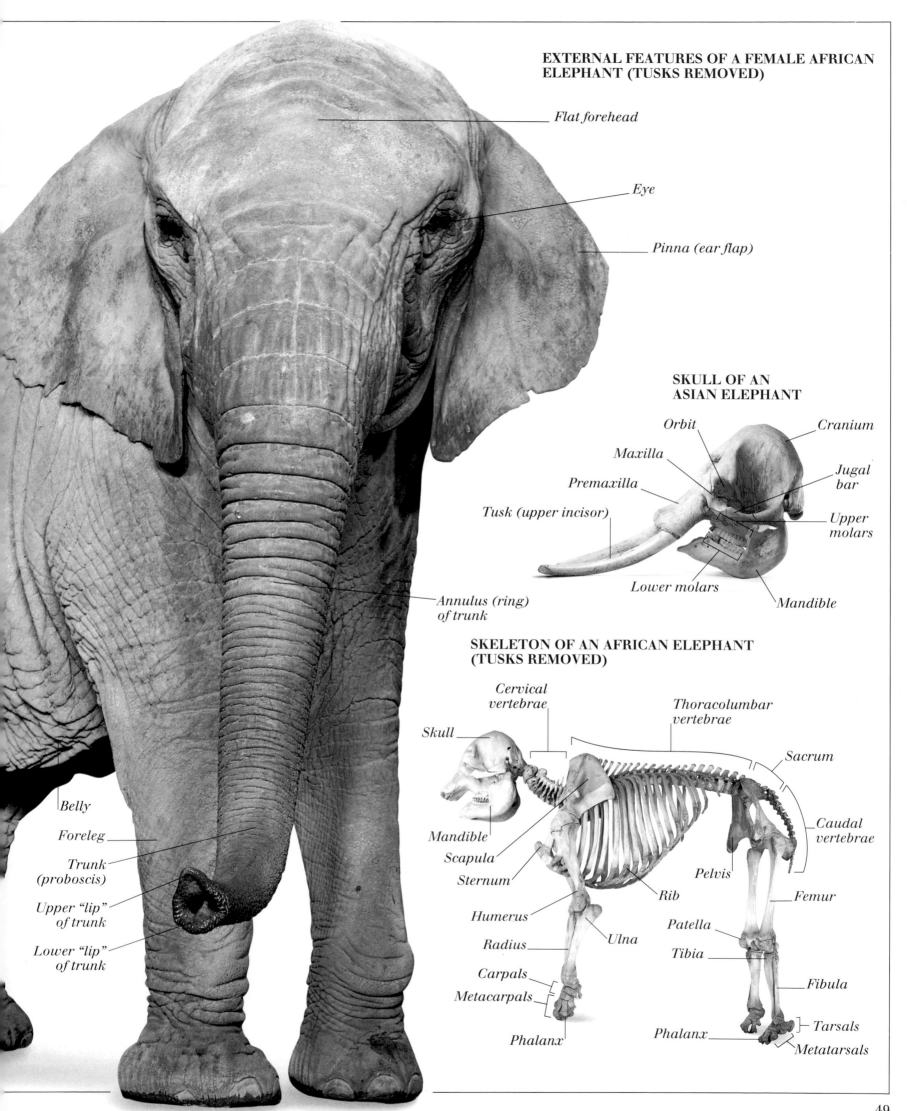

**EXTERNAL FEATURES OF A FEMALE AFRICAN
ELEPHANT (TUSKS REMOVED)**

Flat forehead

Eye

Pinna (ear flap)

Annulus (ring)
of trunk

Belly

Foreleg

Trunk
(proboscis)

Upper "lip"
of trunk

Lower "lip"
of trunk

**SKULL OF AN
ASIAN ELEPHANT**

Orbit

Cranium

Maxilla

Jugal
bar

Premaxilla

Tusk (upper incisor)

Upper
molars

Lower molars

Mandible

**SKELETON OF AN AFRICAN ELEPHANT
(TUSKS REMOVED)**

Cervical
vertebrae

Thoracolumbar
vertebrae

Skull

Sacrum

Mandible

Caudal
vertebrae

Scapula

Sternum

Pelvis

Rib

Femur

Humerus

Patella

Radius

Ulna

Tibia

Carpals

Fibula

Metacarpals

Phalanx

Tarsals

Phalanx

Metatarsals

49

Primates

THE MAMMALIAN ORDER PRIMATES consists of monkeys, apes, and their relatives (including humans). There are two suborders of primates: Prosimii, the primitive primates, which include lemurs, tarsiers, and lorises; and Anthropoidea, the advanced primates, which include monkeys, apes, and humans. The anthropoids are divided into New World monkeys, Old World monkeys, and hominids. New World monkeys typically have wide-apart nostrils that open to the side; and long tails, which are prehensile (grasping) in some species. This group of monkeys lives in South America, and includes marmosets, tamarins, and howler monkeys. Old World monkeys typically have close-set nostrils that open forwards or downwards; and non-prehensile tails. This group of monkeys lives in Africa and Asia, and includes langurs, mandrills, macaques, and baboons. Hominids typically have large brains, and no tail. This group includes the apes—chimpanzees, gibbons, gorillas, and orangutans—and humans.

INTERNAL ANATOMY OF A FEMALE CHIMPANZEE

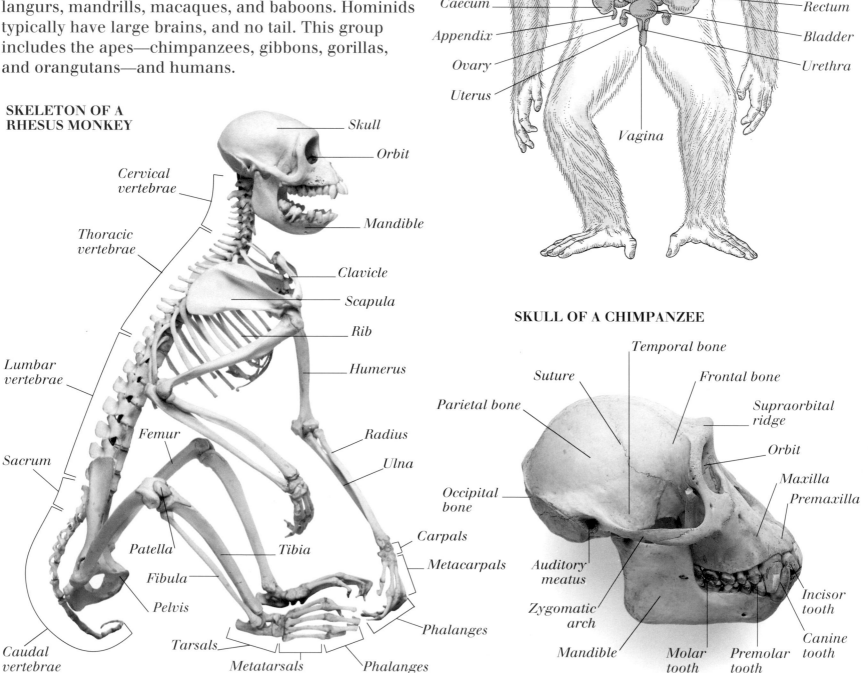

Buccal cavity
Tongue
Trachea
Lung
Liver
Pancreas
Small intestine
Caecum
Appendix
Ovary
Uterus
Vagina
Brain
Nasal cavity
Spinal cord
Oesophagus
Heart
Diaphragm
Stomach
Spleen
Large intestine
Rectum
Bladder
Urethra

SKELETON OF A RHESUS MONKEY

Skull
Orbit
Cervical vertebrae
Mandible
Thoracic vertebrae
Clavicle
Scapula
Rib
Humerus
Lumbar vertebrae
Sacrum
Femur
Radius
Ulna
Patella
Tibia
Fibula
Pelvis
Carpals
Metacarpals
Caudal vertebrae
Tarsals
Metatarsals
Phalanges
Phalanges

SKULL OF A CHIMPANZEE

Temporal bone
Suture
Frontal bone
Parietal bone
Supraorbital ridge
Orbit
Occipital bone
Maxilla
Premaxilla
Auditory meatus
Zygomatic arch
Mandible
Molar tooth
Premolar tooth
Incisor tooth
Canine tooth

EXAMPLES OF PRIMATES

RING-TAILED LEMUR
(Lemur catta)
A prosimian

MALE RED HOWLER MONKEY
(Alouatta seniculus)
A New World monkey

MALE MANDRILL
(Mandrillus sphinx)
An Old World monkey

CHIMPANZEE
(Pan troglodytes)
An ape

EXTERNAL FEATURES OF A YOUNG GORILLA

GOLDEN LION TAMARIN
(Leontopithecus rosalia)
A New World monkey

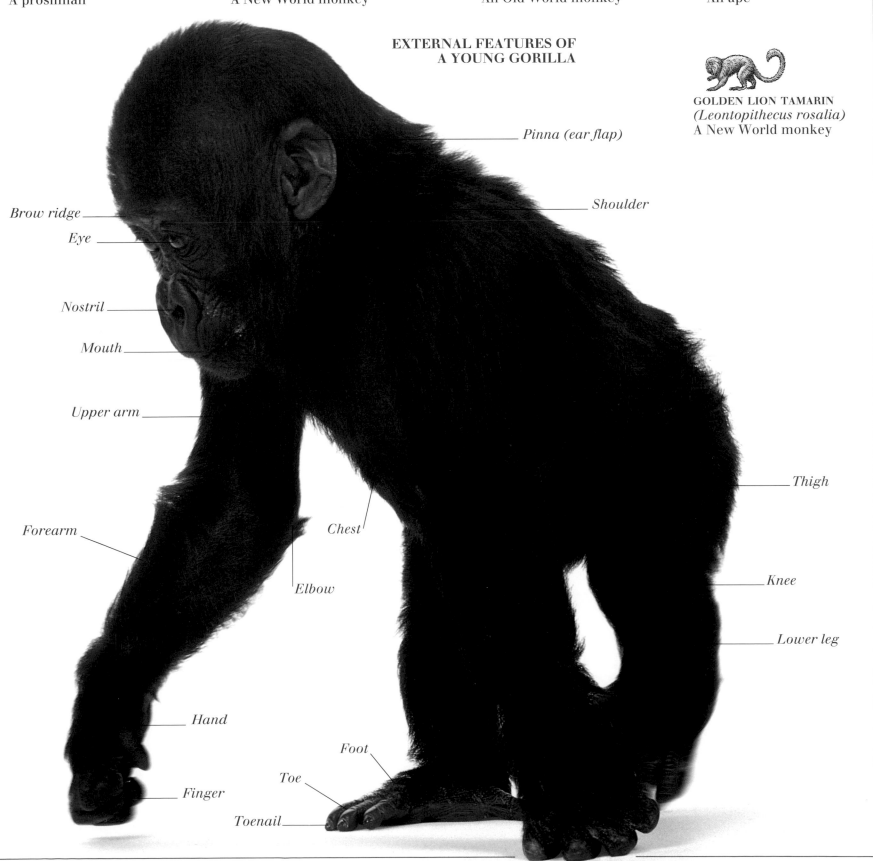

Pinna (ear flap)

Shoulder

Brow ridge

Eye

Nostril

Mouth

Upper arm

Thigh

Forearm

Chest

Elbow

Knee

Lower leg

Hand

Foot

Toe

Finger

Toenail

Dolphins, whales, and seals

DOLPHINS, WHALES, AND SEALS belong to two orders of mammals adapted to living in water. Dolphins and whales make up the order Cetacea. Typical cetacean features include a streamlined, fish-like shape; forelimbs in the form of flippers; no visible hind limbs; a horizontally flattened tail; and thick blubber under the skin. There are two groups of cetaceans: toothed whales, including sperm whales, white whales, beaked whales, dolphins, and porpoises; and the larger whalebone (baleen) whales, including rorquals, grey whales, and right whales. The blue whale—a rorqual—is the largest living animal: an adult may be up to 30 m (100 ft) long and weigh 130 tonnes (128 tons). Seals and their relatives—sea lions and walruses—make up the order Pinnipedia. Characteristically, they have a streamlined, torpedo-shaped body; forelimbs and hind limbs modified as flippers; thick blubber; and no external ears.

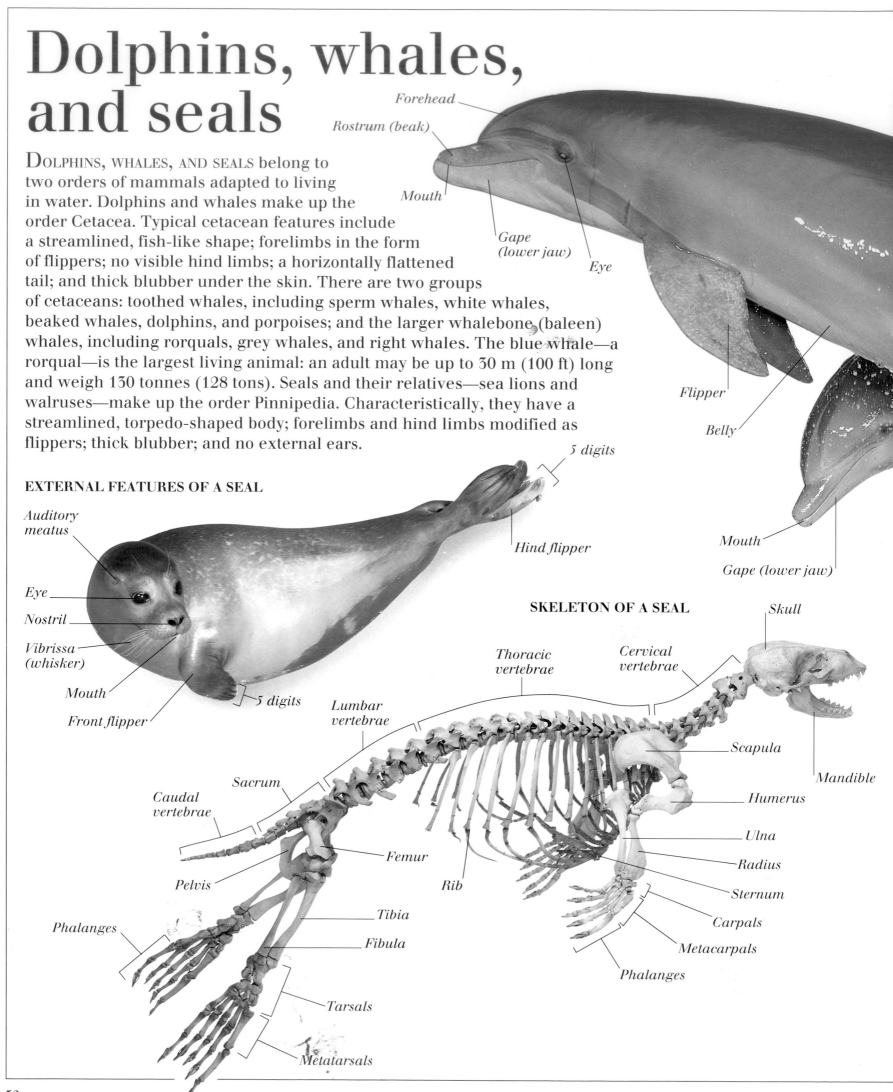

Forehead

Rostrum (beak)

Mouth

Gape (lower jaw)

Eye

Flipper

Belly

Mouth

Gape (lower jaw)

EXTERNAL FEATURES OF A SEAL

Auditory meatus

Eye

Nostril

Vibrissa (whisker)

Mouth

Front flipper

5 digits

Hind flipper

5 digits

SKELETON OF A SEAL

Skull

Thoracic vertebrae

Cervical vertebrae

Lumbar vertebrae

Sacrum

Caudal vertebrae

Pelvis

Femur

Tibia

Fibula

Rib

Phalanges

Tarsals

Metatarsals

Scapula

Mandible

Humerus

Ulna

Radius

Sternum

Carpals

Metacarpals

Phalanges

EXTERNAL FEATURES OF A DOLPHIN

EXAMPLES OF CETACEANS

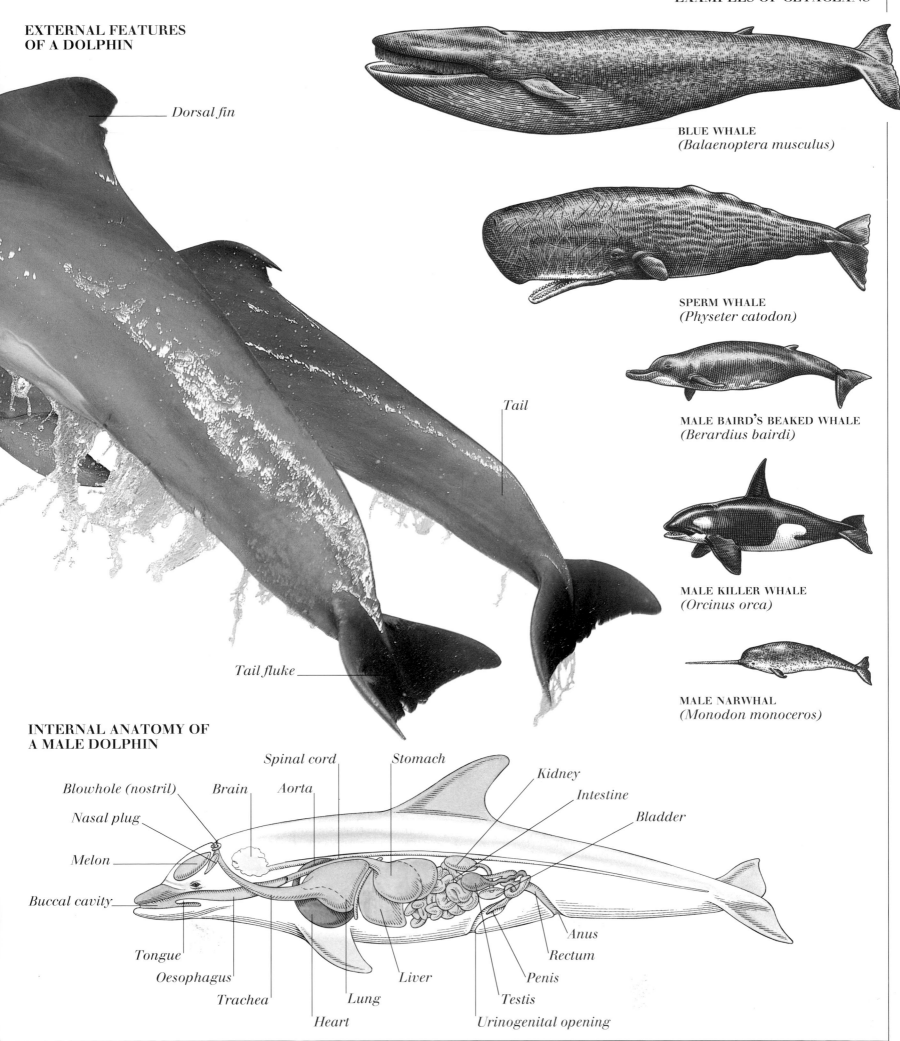

Dorsal fin

Tail

Tail fluke

BLUE WHALE
(*Balaenoptera musculus*)

SPERM WHALE
(*Physeter catodon*)

MALE BAIRD'S BEAKED WHALE
(*Berardius bairdi*)

MALE KILLER WHALE
(*Orcinus orca*)

MALE NARWHAL
(*Monodon monoceros*)

INTERNAL ANATOMY OF A MALE DOLPHIN

Spinal cord

Stomach

Kidney

Blowhole (nostril)

Brain

Aorta

Intestine

Nasal plug

Bladder

Melon

Buccal cavity

Anus

Rectum

Tongue

Penis

Oesophagus

Testis

Trachea

Lung

Heart

Urinogenital opening

Liver

Marsupials and Monotremes

MARSUPIALS AND MONOTREMES are two orders of mammals that differ from other mammalian groups in the ways that their young develop. The order Marsupalia, the pouched mammals, is made up of kangaroos and their relatives. Typically, marsupials give birth to their young at a very early stage of development. The young then crawls to the mother's pouch (which is on the outside of her abdomen), where it attaches itself to a nipple and remains until fully developed. Most marsupials live in Australia, although the opossums—which are classified as marsupials despite not having a pouch—live in the Americas. The order Monotremata is made up of the platypus and its relatives (the echidnas, or spiny anteaters). The monotremes are primitive mammals that lay eggs, which the mother incubates. The monotremes are found only in Australia and New Guinea.

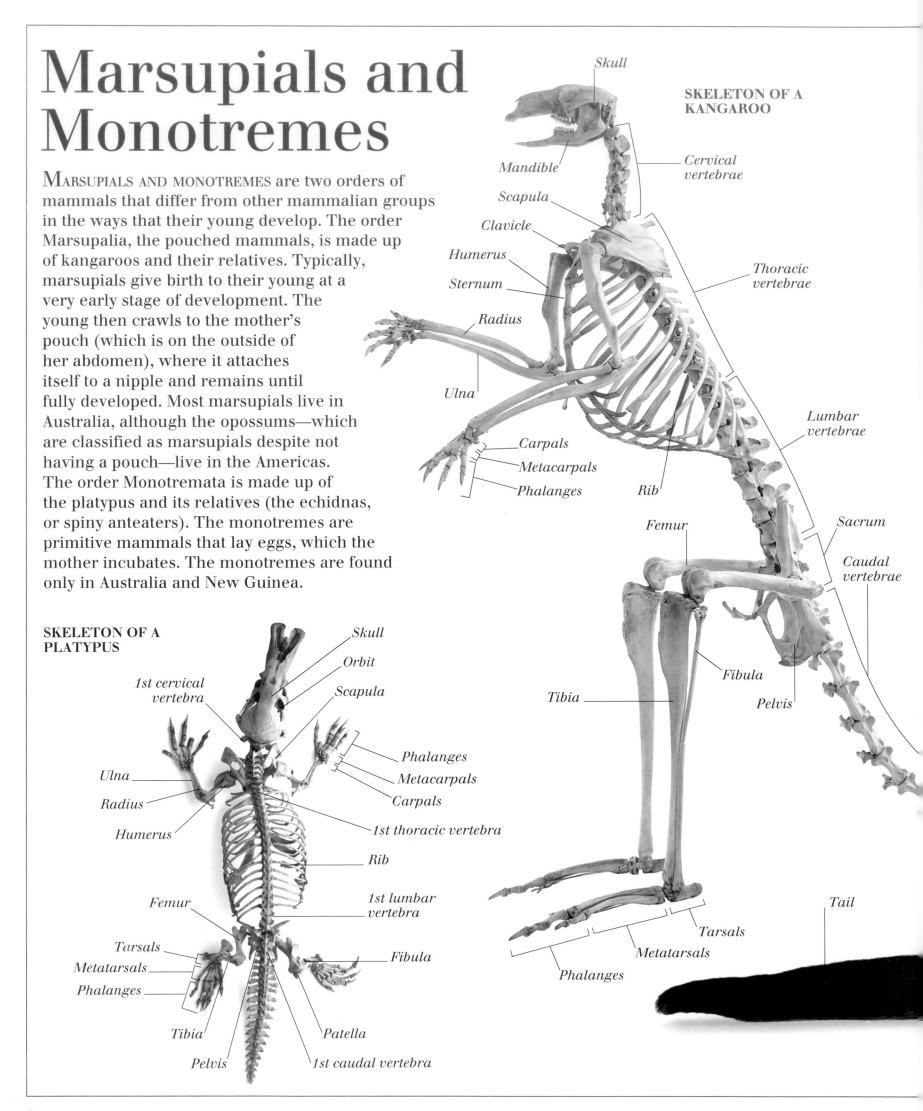

SKELETON OF A KANGAROO

Skull
Mandible
Cervical vertebrae
Scapula
Clavicle
Humerus
Sternum
Radius
Ulna
Carpals
Metacarpals
Phalanges
Rib
Thoracic vertebrae
Lumbar vertebrae
Femur
Sacrum
Caudal vertebrae
Fibula
Tibia
Pelvis
Tarsals
Metatarsals
Phalanges
Tail

SKELETON OF A PLATYPUS

1st cervical vertebra
Skull
Orbit
Scapula
Ulna
Radius
Humerus
Phalanges
Metacarpals
Carpals
1st thoracic vertebra
Rib
1st lumbar vertebra
Femur
Tarsals
Metatarsals
Phalanges
Fibula
Tibia
Patella
Pelvis
1st caudal vertebra

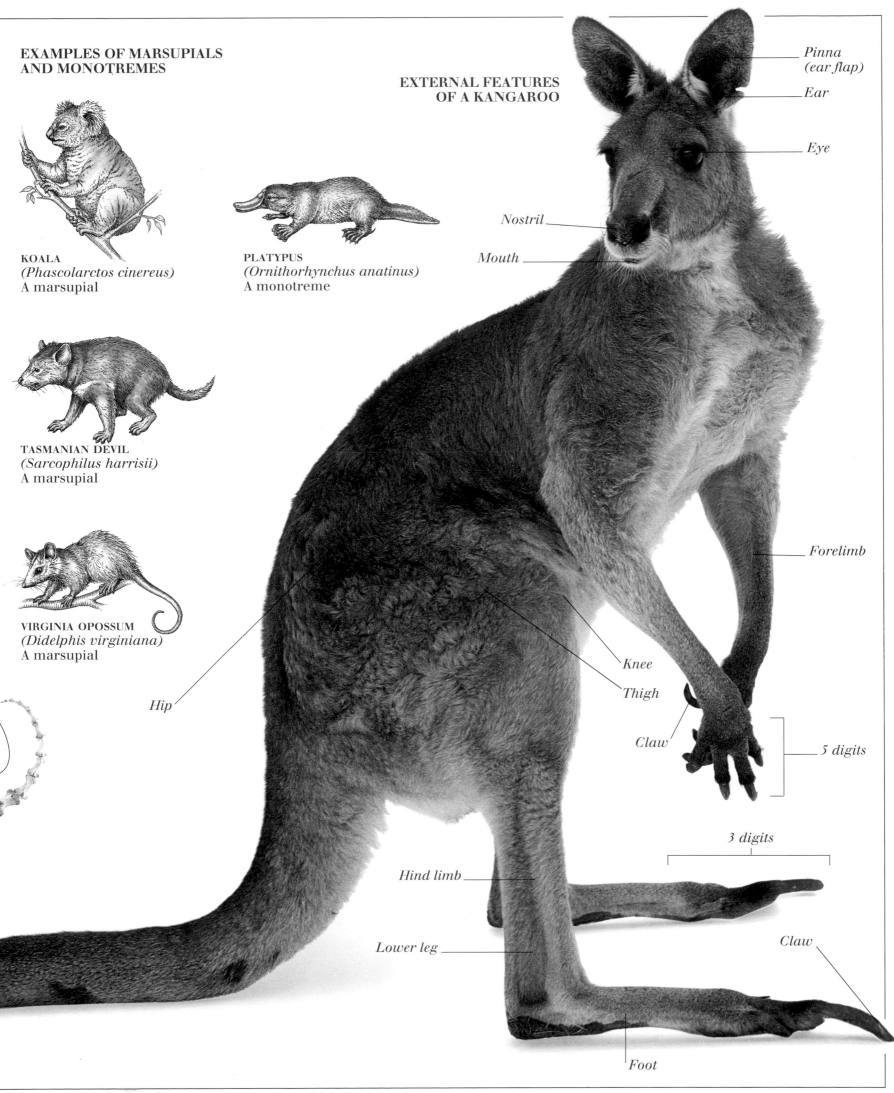

EXAMPLES OF MARSUPIALS AND MONOTREMES

KOALA
(Phascolarctos cinereus)
A marsupial

PLATYPUS
(Ornithorhynchus anatinus)
A monotreme

TASMANIAN DEVIL
(Sarcophilus harrisii)
A marsupial

VIRGINIA OPOSSUM
(Didelphis virginiana)
A marsupial

EXTERNAL FEATURES OF A KANGAROO

*Pinna
(ear flap)*

Ear

Eye

Nostril

Mouth

Forelimb

Knee

Thigh

Claw

5 digits

Hip

3 digits

Hind limb

Lower leg

Claw

Foot

Animal tracks

ANIMAL TRACKS ARE TEMPORARY RECORDS of the passage of land animals across impressionable surfaces, such as damp sand, mud, or snow. By examining tracks for the shape, size, and number of toes, claws, nails, hooves, or pads, it is often possible to identify the animal that made them. For example, the paw marks of mammals that walk on their toes, such as dogs and cats, can be differentiated by the shape and size of their pads. As well as identifying an animal, tracks can often reveal its way of life. For instance, the tracks made by web-footed ducks show that they are swimming birds, whereas the open-toed tracks of crows show that they are perching birds. In addition, the depth and pattern of tracks reveal whether the animal was walking, running, or hopping.

EXAMPLES OF ANIMAL TRACKS

Claw of 3rd toe
Claw of 4th toe
Pad of 3rd toe
Pad of 4th toe
Claw of 2nd toe
Claw of 5th toe
Pad of 2nd toe
Pad of 5th toe
Main pad

RIGHT FOREFOOT OF A DOMESTIC DOG

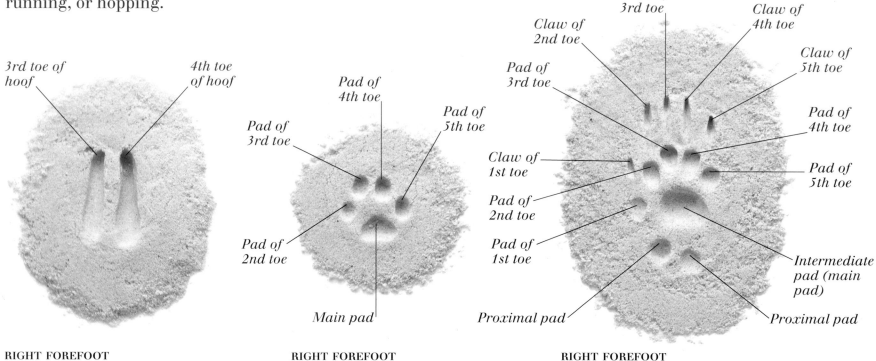

3rd toe of hoof
4th toe of hoof

RIGHT FOREFOOT OF A DOMESTIC SHEEP

Pad of 4th toe
Pad of 5th toe
Pad of 3rd toe
Pad of 2nd toe
Main pad

RIGHT FOREFOOT OF A DOMESTIC CAT

Claw of 3rd toe
Claw of 2nd toe
Claw of 4th toe
Pad of 3rd toe
Claw of 5th toe
Pad of 4th toe
Claw of 1st toe
Pad of 5th toe
Pad of 2nd toe
Pad of 1st toe
Intermediate pad (main pad)
Proximal pad
Proximal pad

RIGHT FOREFOOT OF A BADGER

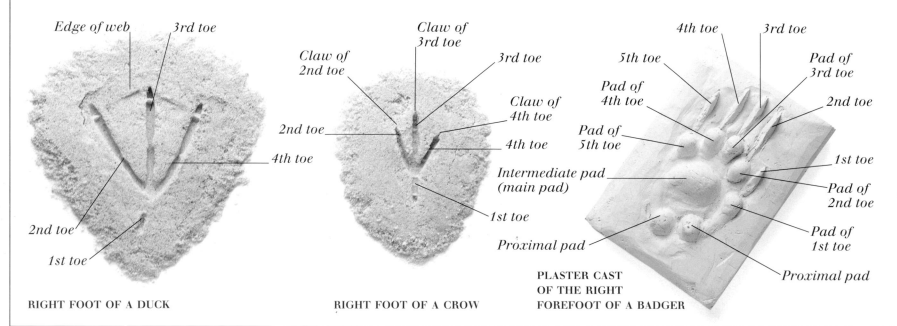

Edge of web
3rd toe
4th toe
2nd toe
1st toe

RIGHT FOOT OF A DUCK

Claw of 3rd toe
Claw of 2nd toe
3rd toe
Claw of 4th toe
2nd toe
4th toe
1st toe

RIGHT FOOT OF A CROW

4th toe
3rd toe
5th toe
Pad of 3rd toe
Pad of 4th toe
2nd toe
Pad of 5th toe
1st toe
Intermediate pad (main pad)
Pad of 2nd toe
Pad of 1st toe
Proximal pad
Proximal pad

PLASTER CAST OF THE RIGHT FOREFOOT OF A BADGER

TRACKS AND MOVEMENT OF A HORSE

WALKING

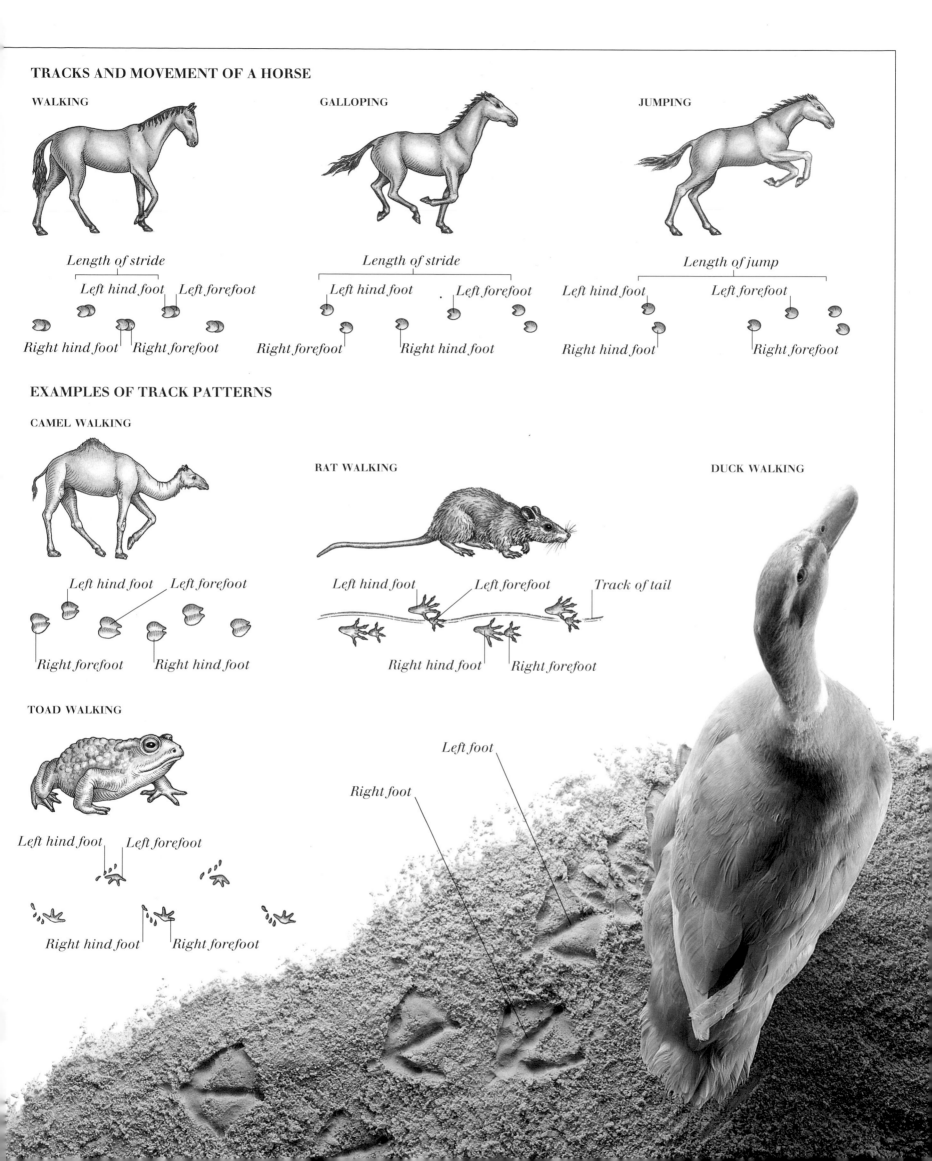

Length of stride

Left hind foot   Left forefoot

Right hind foot   Right forefoot

GALLOPING

Length of stride

Left hind foot   Left forefoot

Right forefoot   Right hind foot

JUMPING

Length of jump

Left hind foot   Left forefoot

Right hind foot   Right forefoot

EXAMPLES OF TRACK PATTERNS

CAMEL WALKING

Left hind foot   Left forefoot

Right forefoot   Right hind foot

RAT WALKING

Left hind foot   Left forefoot   Track of tail

Right hind foot   Right forefoot

DUCK WALKING

TOAD WALKING

Left hind foot   Left forefoot

Right hind foot   Right forefoot

Left foot

Right foot

Animal classification

BIOLOGISTS USE A UNIVERSAL SYSTEM to classify animals and other organisms. All animals form one large grouping, the kingdom Animalia. The kingdom is subdivided into progressively smaller groups on the basis of similarities among animals within each group, and their differences from animals in other groups. The result of this repeated subdivision is a "family tree" of the animal world. First, the kingdom Animalia is divided into several phyla (singular: phylum)—for example, phylum Chordata, which includes all animals with backbones, such as birds, fish, and mammals. Each phylum is divided into classes, and each class into orders. Every order contains a number of families, each of which is split into genera (singular: genus). Finally, each genus is divided into species. In some cases, additional levels of classification may be used. These extra levels are indicated by prefixes, such as "super-" and "sub-". In addition to the formal biological classification, animals are often divided into two main groups: vertebrates and invertebrates. Vertebrates have a backbone (vertebral column), whereas invertebrates do not. The chart shows the main groups in the animal kingdom.

KINGDOM ANIMALIA

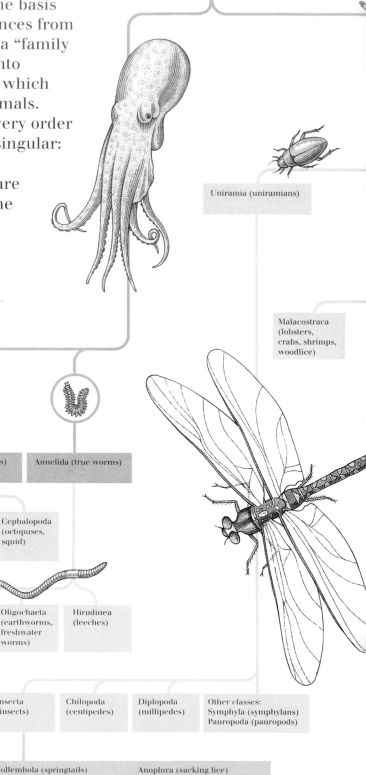

Uniramia (uniramians)

Malacostraca (lobsters, crabs, shrimps, woodlice)

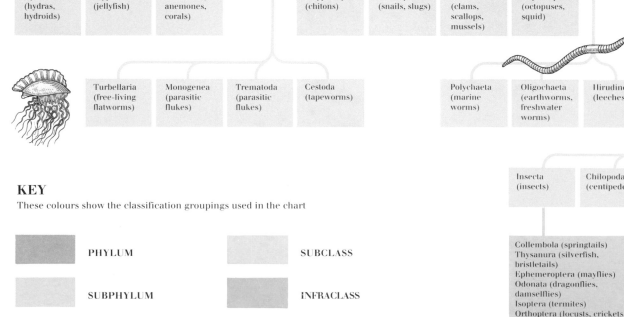

Porifera (sponges)	Cnidaria (coelenterates)	Platyhelminthes (flatworms)	Nematoda (roundworms)	Mollusca (molluscs)	Annelida (true worms)

Hydrozoa (hydras, hydroids)

Scyphozoa (jellyfish)

Anthozoa (sea anemones, corals)

Polyplacophora (chitons)

Gastropoda (snails, slugs)

Bivalvia (clams, scallops, mussels)

Cephalopoda (octopuses, squid)

Turbellaria (free-living flatworms)

Monogenea (parasitic flukes)

Trematoda (parasitic flukes)

Cestoda (tapeworms)

Polychaeta (marine worms)

Oligochaeta (earthworms, freshwater worms)

Hirudinea (leeches)

Insecta (insects)

Chilopoda (centipedes)

Diplopoda (millipedes)

Other classes: Symphyla (symphylans) Pauropoda (pauropods)

KEY

These colours show the classification groupings used in the chart

PHYLUM		SUBCLASS	
SUBPHYLUM		INFRACLASS	
SUPERCLASS		ORDER	
CLASS			

Collembola (springtails)
Thysanura (silverfish, bristletails)
Ephemeroptera (mayflies)
Odonata (dragonflies, damselflies)
Isoptera (termites)
Orthoptera (locusts, crickets, grasshoppers, cockroaches, mantids)
Dermaptera (earwigs)
Phasmida (stick insects, leaf insects)
Psocoptera (booklice, barklice)
Hemiptera (true bugs)

Anoplura (sucking lice)
Mallophaga (biting lice, birdlice)
Homoptera (white flies, aphids, scale insects, cicadas)
Coleoptera (beetles, weevils)
Neuroptera (alder flies, lacewings, ant lions, snake flies, dobsonflies)
Hymenoptera (ants, bees, wasps)
Siphonaptera (fleas)
Diptera (true flies, mosquitoes, gnats)
Lepidoptera (butterflies, moths)

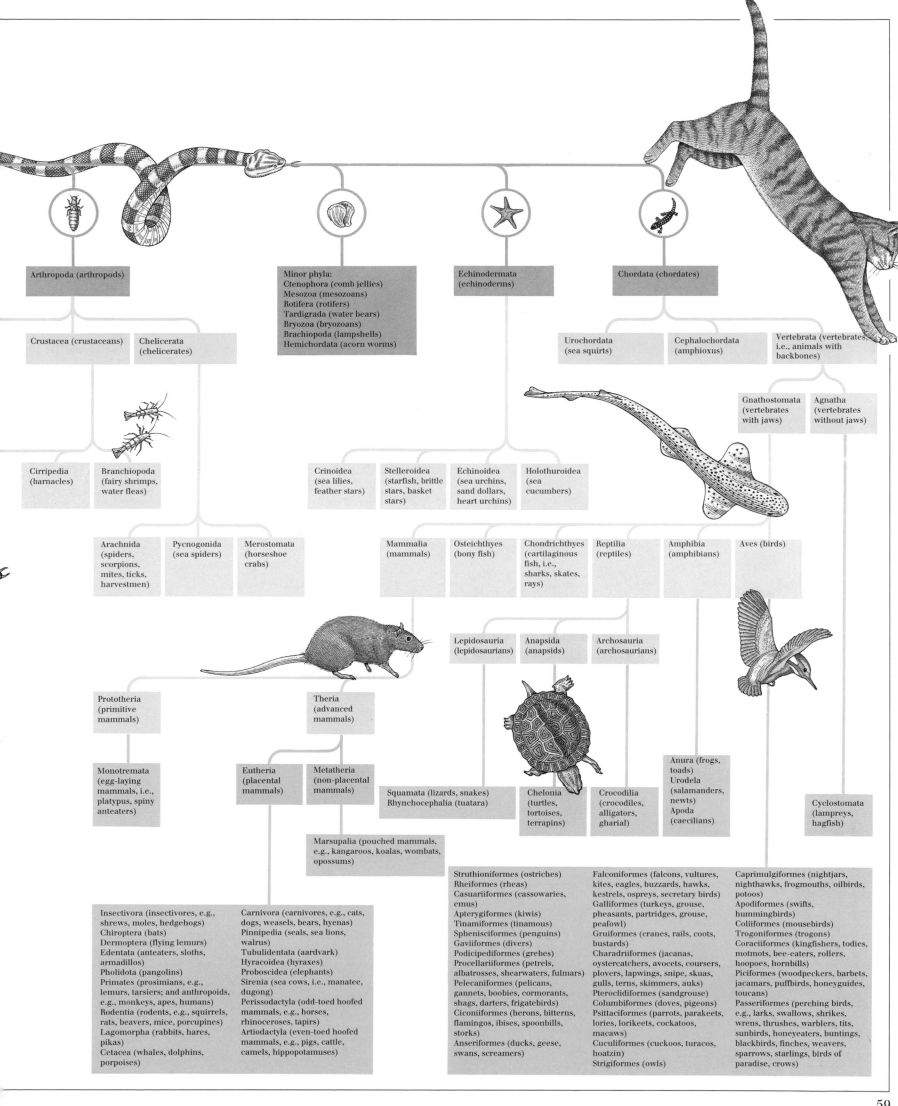

Arthropoda (arthropods)

Crustacea (crustaceans)

Chelicerata (chelicerates)

Minor phyla:
Ctenophora (comb jellies)
Mesozoa (mesozoans)
Rotifera (rotifers)
Tardigrada (water bears)
Bryozoa (bryozoans)
Brachiopoda (lampshells)
Hemichordata (acorn worms)

Echinodermata (echinoderms)

Chordata (chordates)

Urochordata (sea squirts)

Cephalochordata (amphioxus)

Vertebrata (vertebrates, i.e., animals with backbones)

Gnathostomata (vertebrates with jaws)

Agnatha (vertebrates without jaws)

Cirripedia (barnacles)

Branchiopoda (fairy shrimps, water fleas)

Crinoidea (sea lilies, feather stars)

Stelleroidea (starfish, brittle stars, basket stars)

Echinoidea (sea urchins, sand dollars, heart urchins)

Holothuroidea (sea cucumbers)

Arachnida (spiders, scorpions, mites, ticks, harvestmen)

Pycnogonida (sea spiders)

Merostomata (horseshoe crabs)

Mammalia (mammals)

Osteichthyes (bony fish)

Chondrichthyes (cartilaginous fish, i.e., sharks, skates, rays)

Reptilia (reptiles)

Amphibia (amphibians)

Aves (birds)

Lepidosauria (lepidosaurians)

Anapsida (anapsids)

Archosauria (archosaurians)

Prototheria (primitive mammals)

Theria (advanced mammals)

Monotremata (egg-laying mammals, i.e., platypus, spiny anteaters)

Eutheria (placental mammals)

Metatheria (non-placental mammals)

Squamata (lizards, snakes)
Rhynchocephalia (tuatara)

Chelonia (turtles, tortoises, terrapins)

Crocodilia (crocodiles, alligators, gharial)

Anura (frogs, toads)
Urodela (salamanders, newts)
Apoda (caecilians)

Cyclostomata (lampreys, hagfish)

Marsupalia (pouched mammals, e.g., kangaroos, koalas, wombats, opossums)

Insectivora (insectivores, e.g., shrews, moles, hedgehogs)
Chiroptera (bats)
Dermoptera (flying lemurs)
Edentata (anteaters, sloths, armadillos)
Pholidota (pangolins)
Primates (prosimians, e.g., lemurs, tarsiers; and anthropoids, e.g., monkeys, apes, humans)
Rodentia (rodents, e.g., squirrels, rats, beavers, mice, porcupines)
Lagomorpha (rabbits, hares, pikas)
Cetacea (whales, dolphins, porpoises)

Carnivora (carnivores, e.g., cats, dogs, weasels, bears, hyenas)
Pinnipedia (seals, sea lions, walrus)
Tubulidentata (aardvark)
Hyracoidea (hyraxes)
Proboscidea (elephants)
Sirenia (sea cows, i.e., manatee, dugong)
Perissodactyla (odd-toed hoofed mammals, e.g., horses, rhinoceroses, tapirs)
Artiodactyla (even-toed hoofed mammals, e.g., pigs, cattle, camels, hippopotamuses)

Struthioniformes (ostriches)
Rheiformes (rheas)
Casuariiformes (cassowaries, emus)
Apterygiformes (kiwis)
Tinamiformes (tinamous)
Sphenisciformes (penguins)
Gaviiformes (divers)
Podicipediformes (grebes)
Procellariiformes (petrels, albatrosses, shearwaters, fulmars)
Pelecaniformes (pelicans, gannets, boobies, cormorants, shags, darters, frigatebirds)
Ciconiiformes (herons, bitterns, flamingos, ibises, spoonbills, storks)
Anseriformes (ducks, geese, swans, screamers)

Falconiformes (falcons, vultures, kites, eagles, buzzards, hawks, kestrels, ospreys, secretary birds)
Galliformes (turkeys, grouse, pheasants, partridges, grouse, peafowl)
Gruiformes (cranes, rails, coots, bustards)
Charadriiformes (jacanas, oystercatchers, avocets, coursers, plovers, lapwings, snipe, skuas, gulls, terns, skimmers, auks)
Pteroclidiformes (sandgrouse)
Columbiformes (doves, pigeons)
Psittaciformes (parrots, parakeets, lories, lorikeets, cockatoos, macaws)
Cuculiformes (cuckoos, turacos, hoatzin)
Strigiformes (owls)

Caprimulgiformes (nightjars, nighthawks, frogmouths, oilbirds, potoos)
Apodiformes (swifts, hummingbirds)
Coliiformes (mousebirds)
Trogoniformes (trogons)
Coraciiformes (kingfishers, todies, motmots, bee-eaters, rollers, hoopoes, hornbills)
Piciformes (woodpeckers, barbets, jacamars, puffbirds, honeyguides, toucans)
Passeriformes (perching birds, e.g., larks, swallows, shrikes, wrens, thrushes, warblers, tits, sunbirds, honeyeaters, buntings, blackbirds, finches, weavers, sparrows, starlings, birds of paradise, crows)

Index

Acknowledgments

Dorling Kindersley would like to thank:
David Manning's Animal Ark; Intellectual Animals; Howletts Zoo, Canterbury; John Dunlop; Alexander O'Donnell; Sue Evans at the Royal Veterinary College, London; Dr.Geoff Potts and Fred Frettsome at the Marine Biological Association of the United Kingdom, Plymouth; Jeremy Adams at the Booth Museum of Natural History, Brighton; Derek Telling at the Department of Anatomy, University of Bristol; the Natural History Museum, London; Andy Highfield at the Tortoise Trust; Brian Harris at the Aquarium, London Zoo; the Invertebrate Department, London Zoo; Dr Harold McClure at the Yerkes Regional Primate Research Center, Emory University, Atlanta, Georgia;

Nielson Lausen at the Harvard Medical School, New England Regional Primates Research Center, Southborough, Massachusetts; Dr Paul Hopwood at the Department of Veterinary Anatomy, University of Sydney; Dean Franklin; Roy Flooks

Additional photography:
Steve Gorton, Tim Ridley, Jane Burton, Matthew Ward, Jerry Young, Judith Harrington, Cyril Laubscher, Bob Langrish

Additional design assistance:
Simone End, Nicki Liddiard

Additional editorial assistance:
Christine Murdock, Louise Tucker

Illustrators:
John Woodcock, Simone End, David Hopkins, Sandra Pond, Nick Loates, Roy Flooks

Picture credits:
t=top b=bottom c=centre l=left r=right
Oxford Scientific Films/Animals Animals/Breck P. Kent: 16cl; 25tl /London Scientific Films: 16tr; 17tc. Sinclair Stammers/Science Photo Library: 17cb

Index:
Irene Lyford

Picture research:
Clive Webster